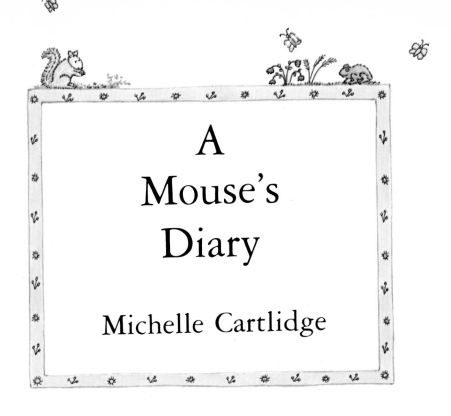

A Mouse's Diary

Michelle Cartlidge

Lothrop, Lee & Shepard Books
New York

Also by Michelle Cartlidge

The Bears' Bazaar
Teddy Trucks

Library of Congress Cataloging in Publication Data
Cartlidge, Michelle.   A mouse's diary.
Summary: A young mouse writes about her ballet class, a shopping trip, the end-of-term party, and other events in her life.
[1. Mice—Fiction] I. Title.   PZ7.C249Mo   1983   [E]   80-17060
ISBN 0-688-41987-9   AACR1   ISBN 0-688-51987-3 (lib. bdg.)

My Diary
Mousefield School
Summer Term

Sunday

I went to the park with my father and mother and younger brother. We had a lovely picnic. Some tiny birds hopped up to us, wanting something to eat, and we fed them crumbs of bread. My brother tried to catch one, but he couldn't. They just flew away.

Monday

At ballet class today we pretended to
be candles on a great big birthday
cake. The teacher said we looked more
like scarecrows than pretty candles. In
the middle of the dancing I had to stop
and change over my ballet shoes
because they were on the wrong feet.

Tuesday

After school my mother took us to the
toy shop. First I wanted to buy the
pink elephant. Then I saw the doll
furniture and I chose a chair and a
wardrobe for my dollhouse. My
brother bought a little wooden train.
We spent all our pocket money.

Wednesday

The whole class went out on a Nature Find. We saw squirrels high up in the trees. We found leaves of different shapes and colors. I saw some tiny frogs and tried to catch butterflies. Back at school we labeled everything for our Nature Table.

Thursday

My brother and I played dressing up.
He was a Viking and I was a smart
lady in a long silky dress. I put on lots
of red lipstick. Then my brother
dressed up as a ghost. He made
horrible noises, but I wasn't
frightened. My mother wasn't very
pleased when she saw all the mess we
had made.

Friday

While we were playing
in the street, we saw a
big moving van outside
one of the houses. We
watched all the furniture
being loaded into the van.
The moving mice were very
careful not to drop anything. We
giggled when we noticed other mice
peering out of their windows to see
what was going on.

Saturday

My best friend came to play. She lives next door to me and we sit next to each other in class. It rained all day, so my mother took us to the cake shop for a treat. I had a large creamy cake with a cherry on top and my friend had a chocolate one.

Sunday

On Sunday mornings my parents like reading the newspapers, so we have to keep out of their way. We had a terrific pillow fight. I was squashed flat on the floor. There were feathers flying everywhere. My naughty brother ripped a pillow by mistake and we had a lot of clearing up to do.

Monday

My best friend came again today.
I showed her my new doll furniture
and we played with my dollhouse.
We put two dolls upstairs in bed
ready for their goodnight story, and
one doll in front of the mirror. Then
I put two more dolls in the kitchen
to have their supper. We sat the other
two in armchairs by the fire.

Tuesday

The whole class went to the library for story time. We heard about an elephant that runs away from the jungle and meets a very rich old lady who lives in the town. Then we all chose books to look at. I pulled one off the shelf and a whole lot fell down with a big bang on the floor. We are supposed to be very quiet in the library.

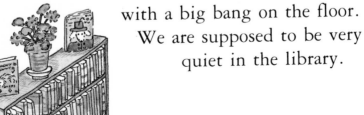

Wednesday

Today a postcard came from my granny. We are going to tea with her on Saturday. After school we went to the pond, because my brother wanted to feed the ducks. They were very hungry and kept on quacking for more. We saw some fluffy yellow ducklings far across the pond. They swam to meet us too.

Thursday

Tomorrow is the last day of school and
we are having a Punch and Judy show
and a party tea. Today our teacher
showed us how to make place mats and
hats out of crepe paper for the party.
My best friend and I tried on our hats
to see how they looked. I'm so excited,
I can't wait until tomorrow.

Friday

The Punch and Judy show came today.
There was a little brown dog called
Toby, who did lots of funny tricks. He
even did a dance for us. Mr. Punch was
naughty and held his baby upside
down. We were all frightened when the
crocodile came out from under the
curtain and snapped. Then
we had our party tea and
wore our paper hats.

Saturday

Today we went to see Granny and I told her all about the party and the Punch and Judy show. Then my brother and I played hide and seek around her plants, peeping at each other through the leaves. We knocked over one of the best plants, and poor Granny was very upset. We said we were sorry and would be more careful next time.

Sunday

Now I have filled up my diary, I am going to read it to my toys for their special goodnight story.

Ergebnisse der Mathematik und ihrer Grenzgebiete 96

A Series of Modern Surveys in Mathematics

P. R. Halmos V. S. Sunder

Bounded Integral Operators on L^2 Spaces

Springer-Verlag
Berlin Heidelberg New York 1978

Paul Richard Halmos
Indiana University, Bloomington, IN 47401, U.S.A.

Viakalathur Shankar Sunder
University of California, Santa Barbara, CA 93106, U.S.A.

AMS Subject Classification (1970): 47-02, 45-02

ISBN 3-540-08894-6 Springer-Verlag Berlin Heidelberg New York
ISBN 0-387-08894-6 Springer-Verlag New York Heidelberg Berlin

Preface

The subject. The phrase "integral operator" (like some other mathematically informal phrases, such as "effective procedure" and "geometric construction") is sometimes defined and sometimes not. When it is defined, the definition is likely to vary from author to author. While the definition almost always involves an integral, most of its other features can vary quite considerably. Superimposed limiting operations may enter (such as L^2 limits in the theory of Fourier transforms and principal values in the theory of singular integrals), L^p spaces and abstract Banach spaces may intervene, a scalar may be added (as in the theory of the so-called integral operators of the second kind), or, more generally, a multiplication operator may be added (as in the theory of the so-called integral operators of the third kind). The definition used in this book is the most special of all. According to it an integral operator is the natural "continuous" generalization of the operators induced by matrices, and the only integrals that appear are the familiar Lebesgue-Stieltjes integrals on classical non-pathological measure spaces.

The category. Some of the flavor of the theory can be perceived in finite-dimensional linear algebra. Matrices are sometimes considered to be an unnatural and notationally inelegant way of looking at linear transformations. From the point of view of this book that judgement misses something. Abstract vector spaces are the objects of an interesting and useful category; coordinatized vector spaces (spaces of functions with values in the ground field) are the objects of another. The representability of the former by the latter is a powerful tool for the study of the former and the source of deep insight into the computational aspects of the latter. Similarly, more generally, it is the purpose of this book to use function spaces and their natural transformations as a tool for the study of operators on certain abstract vector spaces, and, at the same time, to gain insight into the structure of certain integrals via the operators that they define. In other words, the category to be studied (operator theory) is enriched (made more special) by the addition of extraneous structure (measure), and the enrichment produces new problems — problems that cannot be formulated in the stark, pure category.

Motivation. Why should one study integral operators? The traditional answers are that integral *equations* have important applications outside of mathematics (both directly and through differential equations), and that, from the point of view of pure mathematics, they are the proper extension to analysis of the concepts and methods of the classical algebraic theory of linear equations. A third possible answer is that (for the two reasons just mentioned) the theory of integral operators is the source of all modern functional analysis and remains to this day a rich source of non-trivial examples. Since the major obstacle to progress in many parts of operator theory is the dearth of concrete examples whose properties can be explicitly determined, a systematic theory of integral operators offers new hope for new insights.

The questions. The study does not strive for maximum generality. It is restricted, to begin with, to *linear* transformations only; most of the transformations to be considered will be *bounded* operators; and, finally, the domains of the operators will be *Hilbert* spaces (i.e., L^2 spaces, and not L^p for $p \neq 2$). A rich theory remains even after all these specializations, and there is also much that is not yet known and is in need of being sorted out.

The book does not, of course, answer all questions about integral operators, not even about the special ones (bounded, linear, on L^2) that it is restricted to. We hope that it makes a contribution to the systematization of the theory. Frequently, when the systematic treatment encounters unanswered questions, we indicate, at the appropriate place in the logical development, exactly where such questions arise, how they are connected with others, and what partial information about them is available. The emphasis in the treatment is on the basic implication relations on which the subject rests, rather than on its mechanical techniques. "Which operators can be represented as integral operators?" and "which important sets of integral operators are subsets of which others?" —problems such as these are central, rather than the ones arising from the solutions of integral equations.

Compactness. Many algebraically minded operator theorists are suspicious of the theory of integral operators: they think it is too special. The reason for the suspicion is in the history of the subject: in addition to the unbounded operators that frequently arise in applied mathematics, the integral operators that have received the most attention are the (compact) Hilbert-Schmidt operators. The result is that some operator theorists have the feeling that most (all?) integral operators are compact (and hence not very interesting). That feeling is both wrong and right. It is wrong as it stands: if A is an arbitrary bounded operator, then some scalar translates of A (i.e., operators of the form $A + \lambda$) are representable as integral operators, and such translates are only rarely compact. The feeling is right, however, in a surprising sense. There is another kind of compactness (the $\langle 2, 1 \rangle$ compactness discussed in §13) that is possessed by every integral operator (provided only that the underlying measures are not infinite), and that kind of compactness turns out to be the most powerful single tool in the subject.

Organization. The book is divided into 17 sections. The first five concern the definitions and the examples that are needed throughout. The topics are: description of the kind of measure spaces to be considered, definition of kernels and the operations on them, a quick look at unboundedness (peripheral to the central theme of this book), and then the basic examples from classical analysis.

Sections 6–9 are about constructions: they describe what can and what cannot be done with integral operators. The topics are the possibility of transforming integral operators by measure-theoretic isomorphisms, the correspondence (injective but not surjective) from kernels to operators, and the extent to which that correspondence preserves the algebraic operations (including tensor multiplication) on kernels.

Sections 10 and 11 describe the two most important classes of kernels (absolutely bounded kernels and Carleman kernels), and discuss the properties of each and the implication relations between them.

Sections 12–14 provide some necessary tools from operator theory: a discussion of two different kinds of compactness, and the properties of the essential spectrum, culminating in the celebrated Weyl-von Neumann theorem on the possibility of a kind of generalized diagonalization for Hermitian operators on infinite-dimensional Hilbert spaces.

The climax, the reason for the existence of the book, is reached in the last three sections. They ask (in that order): which operators *can* be integral, which operators *must* be integral, and which operators *are* integral? The "can" question (which operators are unitarily equivalent to an integral operator on a prescribed measure space?) has a complete and satisfactory answer, which is in direct continuation of the pioneering work of von Neumann. The "must" question (which unitary orbits consist of integral operators only?) has a satisfactory partial answer; some closely related special questions (notably about absolutely bounded kernels) remain open. The "are" question (which operators on an L^2 space are induced by a kernel?) has nothing to do with unitary equivalence; it looks at each particular operator as it stands and asks for a way of recognizing that it is (or is not) integral. Here the answer is only half satisfactory: various interesting and useful sufficient conditions are available, but none of them is both necessary and sufficient.

There are three appendices devoted to small digressions: the first is about measure-theoretic pathology, the second is about some pathologically large integrals, and the third contains a proof of the Riemann-Lebesgue lemma, which, among the principal analytic tools that are used, is not frequently a part of modern introductory courses on analysis.

That is the end of the book. The book, however, contains only a part of a large subject, with only one of several approaches, and with explicit mention of only a few of the many challenging problems that are still open.

Conventions

Certain conventions, some linguistic and notational and others typographical, are collected here, to avoid misunderstanding and confusion. All measure spaces are assumed to be σ-finite and separable (except in Appendix A). They are almost always denoted by X and Y, with measures μ and ν. The letter χ is reserved for characteristic functions of sets. Integrals are indicated by the classical differential notation ($\int f(x)\,dx$) whenever the measure remains fixed and plays no special role; when necessary, the measure-theoretic differential ($\int f(x)\,d\mu(x)$) is used instead. If A is an operator on a function space, then the value of the function Af at x is indicated by $Af(x)$ (instead of the more detailed symbol $[Af](x)$). Ordered pairs are indicated by angular brackets $\langle x, y \rangle$; parentheses (f, g) are reserved for inner products. Exception: values of a function of two variables are indicated by $f(x, y)$, not $f(\langle x, y \rangle)$.

Comments on the text are made in a section called Notes; their existence is indicated in the text by a raised number (such as [99]) that refers to the appropriate note. In the Notes, the page next to the number refers back to the point in the text where the reference occurs. Most of the notes are concerned with bibliographical matters.

The symbols ▶ and ◀ (sometimes called "tombstones") are used to indicate the beginning and the end of a discussion respectively. Most frequently ▶ stands for "Proof" and ◀ for "Q.E.D.", so that browsers, who want to know what is being said but do not demand to know why, can skip to their hearts' content.

Prerequisites

The main prerequisite for an uninterrupted reading of the book is familiarity with the standard facts of measure theory and operator theory, as they are likely to be treated in introductory graduate courses on those subjects. Thus, for instance, as far as measure theory is concerned, the reader should know Fatou's lemma, the Lebesgue dominated convergence theorem, the Riesz-Fischer theorem, Fubini's theorem, and the Radon-Nikodym theorem. In addition, the reader should either know, be willing to take on faith, or be willing to look up the representation theorem for finite separable measure spaces with no atoms (by a finite interval in the line). From operator theory the principal necessary concepts are some from general functional analysis (e.g., compact operators, closed operators, and the closed graph theorem), and some from Hilbert space theory (notably the polar decomposition and the spectral theorem).

Contents

§1. Measure Spaces

A matrix is a function. A complex $m \times n$ (rectangular) matrix, for example, is a function a from the Cartesian product $\{1, \dots, m\} \times \{1, \dots, n\}$ to the set $\mathbb{C}$ of complex numbers; its value at the ordered pair $\langle i, j \rangle$ is usually denoted by a_{ij}. In this book it will always be denoted by the typographically and conceptually more convenient symbol $a(i, j)$.

The main reason for studying matrices is their use in linear algebra. They are not only the source of the whole subject, and illuminating examples, but they turn out to be the general case: all facts and all problems about linear transformations can be expressed in terms of their matrix representation.

A matrix a induces a linear transformation A on vectors f in $\mathbb{C}^n$; the action of A is defined by

$$Af(i) = \sum_{j=1}^{n} a(i, j) f(j).$$

(A vector f in $\mathbb{C}^n$ is a complex-valued function on $\{1, \dots, n\}$; its value at j is denoted, of course, by $f(j)$.) The symbol $Af(i)$ might be thought ambiguous at first glance: does it mean $A[f(i)]$ or $[Af](i)$? The former possibility, however, is meaningless — a linear transformation on $\mathbb{C}^n$ acts on vectors, not scalars — and, consequently, the latter is what will always be meant. The same notational convention — $Af(x)$ for $[Af](x)$ — will be used for all operators on function spaces.

The source of most of modern analysis (functional analysis, operator theory) is the theory of "integral equations", which is, in other words, the theory of operators induced by integral "kernels". Kernels are the natural infinite generalization of matrices: they are the objects obtained when the sums occurring in matrix theory are replaced by integrals. There is a more naive generalization of finite matrix theory, namely infinite matrix theory (replace finite sums by infinite ones), but it's not good enough. Integrals include both finite and infinite sums as special cases, but the special cases are too special for the intended contact with other subjects.

Where there is an integral, there is a measure. Like most proverbs, old or *ad hoc*, this one is a little false, but in its present application it is more than a little true. The integral operators studied in this book act on the L^2 of a measure space. Before the systematic study can begin, it is necessary to describe the kinds of measures that are needed for a theory that is general enough to be useful and special enough to be tractable.

The best known examples of measure spaces are (a) the ones that consist of a finite or countably infinite set of points each with a positive mass, (b) the ones that consist of a finite or infinite sub-interval of the line with Lebesgue measure, and (c) the mixed types obtained by the formation of the disjoint union of one of the first type and one of the second. These examples are enough: all classical measure spaces are measure-theoretically isomorphic to one of them.

The last statement is an abbreviated theorem, of course. The unabbreviated version asserts that every measure space is the disjoint union of an *atomic* measure space and a *divisible* one, and it goes on, under suitable countability hypotheses, to represent the two kinds in the concrete ways described above.

An *atom* of a measure space is a set of positive measure that is not the disjoint union of two sets of positive measure. A typical example of an atom is a single point with positive mass. A different example is an uncountable set whose measurable subsets are, by definition, just the countable sets and their comple-ments, with the measure of a set defined to be 0 or ∞ according as the set is countable or co-countable.

An uncountable set all whose subsets are measurable, with the measure of a set defined to be 0 or ∞ according as the set is countable or not, is *not* an atom. This non-example has the property that it has no subsets of strictly smaller but still positive measure — a property that is sometimes used as an alternative definition of atom. For σ-finite measure spaces (to be defined presently) the two definitions are equivalent. A measure space is *atomic* if for each set E of positive measure there exists an atom E_0 such that $E_0 \subset E$. A measure space is *divisible* if it has no atoms at all. ("Divisible" seems to be the most practical antonym of "atomic". "Non-atomic" is more explicit but is harder to distinguish from "not atomic", and the difference is important. The difference is the one between "never" and "sometimes". A space that is atomic has no divisible subsets; a space that is not atomic has a divisible subset, but it may have atoms too.)

The suitable countability hypothesis for atomic measure spaces is easy to state: it is just that the measure space be σ-*finite*, i.e., that the space be the union of countably many sets of finite measure. For divisible measure spaces that hypothesis is not enough: to get representation by Lebesgue measure, it must be assumed, in addition to σ-finiteness, that the measure space is separable.

To say that a measure space X (or, in different but equivalent language, a measure μ) is *separable* means that the Hilbert space $L^2(X)$ $(= L^2(\mu))$ is separa-ble. (The exponent 2 plays no special role here; it can be replaced by any p with $1 \leq p < \infty$. Equivalently: consider the metric space of measurable sets of finite measure, modulo sets of measure zero, with distance defined by the measure of the symmetric difference, and call the measure space separable if that metric space is separable.) Some students, and sometimes even experts from another part of analysis who visit measure theory, are more surprised than pleased to learn that σ-finiteness and separability are independent conditions: anyone who wants both of them must explicitly assume them both.

Example 1.1. ▶ Start with any separable measure space (a pleasant classical one, or, if desired, one as degenerate as the empty set), and adjoin to it an atom of infinite mass. Every integrable function on the enlarged space has to vanish almost everywhere on the adjoined set; it follows that the enlarged space is just as separable as the original one, but, of course, it is not σ-finite. ◄

Example 1.2. ▶ Consider the two-point measure space $\{-1, +1\}$, where each of the two points has mass $\frac{1}{2}$, and form the Cartesian product of uncountably many copies of that space. The result is a space of finite measure (a fortiori σ-finite), but it is not separable. ◄

Now back to the principal theme. The representation theorem for divisible measure spaces asserts that if the measure is σ-finite and separable, then the space is isomorphic to a subinterval of the line.[1] Isomorphism in this context is meant in the sense of measure algebras: there is a one-to-one correspondence between the collections of measurable sets modulo sets of measure zero that preserves the numerical values of the measures and preserves complementation and the formation of countable unions and intersections.

In the study of integral operators the pathology of measure theory is an irrelevant distraction. The representation theorem says that the healthy classical spaces are models for everything that can happen. In the sequel the underlying measure spaces are always assumed to be separable and σ-finite, and, consequently, they can be replaced by "classical" spaces whenever that seems desirable, with no loss of generality.

For present purposes that is all that *must* be said about finiteness and countability conditions on the underlying measures; a little more of what *can* be said is discussed in Appendix A.

§2. Kernels

From now on X and Y will be measure spaces, with measures μ and v. The measure spaces that play the most important roles in the theory are $\mathbb{Z}$, $\mathbb{Z}_+$, $\mathbb{Z}_n$, $\mathbb{R}$, $\mathbb{R}_+$, and $\mathbb{I}$. Explanation: $\mathbb{Z}$ is the set of all integers, $\mathbb{Z}_+$ is the set of non-negative integers, and $\mathbb{Z}_n$ is the set of integers between 1 and n inclusive ($n = 1, 2, 3, \ldots$); in all these cases the measure is the counting measure defined on the class of all subsets; $\mathbb{R}$ is the set of all real numbers, $\mathbb{R}_+$ is the set of non-negative real numbers, and $\mathbb{I}$ is the unit interval, i.e., the set of real numbers between 0 and 1 inclusive; in all these cases the measure is Lebesgue measure defined on the class of all Borel sets. This notation (including X, Y, μ, and v) will be fixed throughout.

A *kernel* is a complex-valued measurable function on the Cartesian product $X \times Y$. The best known examples are of course matrices, defined on $\mathbb{Z}_m \times \mathbb{Z}_n$. Matrices have algebraic structure; they can be added and multiplied and transposed, and they are amenable to other, less popular, but almost equally useful operations such as direct sum, tensor product (direct or Kronecker product), and pointwise product (Hadamard or Schur product). All these concepts can be generalized to arbitrary kernels, sometimes well and sometimes just barely.

If h and k are kernels on $X \times Y$, then the function s defined by

$$s(x, y) = h(x, y) + k(x, y)$$

is a kernel on $X \times Y$, the (pointwise) *sum* of h and k. The kernel p defined by

$$p(x, y) = h(x, y) k(x, y)$$

is the *pointwise product* of h and k. It is less important, but it does come up from time to time. Two especially useful special cases of it are the kernels defined by

$$p(x, y) = \varphi(x) k(x, y)$$

and

$$p(x, y) = k(x, y) \psi(y),$$

where φ and ψ are measurable functions on X and Y respectively.

The *conjugate transpose* of a kernel k on $X \times Y$ is the kernel k^* on $Y \times X$ defined by

$$k^*(y, x) = \overline{k(x, y)}.$$

The *disjoint union* $X \oplus X'$ of two sets X and X' is (as always) the union of "disjoint copies" of X and X'. The idea is just to form the union if the two sets are disjoint, but, if they are not disjoint, then first "make them disjoint" and then form the union. The standard way to make X and X' disjoint is to replace them by $X \times \{0\}$ and $X' \times \{1\}$, and identify each x in X with $\langle x, 0 \rangle$ in $X \times \{0\}$ and each x' in X' with $\langle x', 1 \rangle$ in $X' \times \{1\}$. It is convenient, once the identification is made, to forget that things were ever different, and to pretend that X and X' were, in fact, disjoint all along. If X and X' are measure spaces, then their disjoint union becomes a measure space if the measurable sets are declared to be the sets of the form $F \cup F'$, with F measurable in X and F' measurable in X', and if the measure of such a set is defined to be $\mu(F) + \mu'(F')$.

If k and k' are kernels on $X \times Y$ and $X' \times Y'$ respectively, then their *direct sum* is the kernel $k \oplus k'$ defined on $(X \oplus X') \times (Y \oplus Y')$ by

$$(k \oplus k')(x, y) = k(x, y),$$
$$(k \oplus k')(x', y') = k'(x', y'),$$
$$(k \oplus k')(x, y') = (k \oplus k')(x', y) = 0,$$

whenever $\langle x, y \rangle \in X \times Y$ and $\langle x', y' \rangle \in X' \times Y'$. For matrices a and a', of sizes $m \times n$ and $m' \times n'$, the direct sum has size $(m+m') \times (n+n')$; it has a and a' on the diagonal (as the top left $m \times n$ corner and the bottom right $m' \times n'$ corner) and 0's elsewhere.

It is easy and useful to generalize the concept of direct sum to any finite number of summands, and even to infinitely many. (Even uncountable infinities are manageable, but the standing assumptions of σ-finiteness and separability rule them out here.) If J is an index set and k_j is, for each j in J, a kernel on $X_j \times Y_j$, then form the disjoint union $X = \sum_j \oplus X_j$ of all the X_j's, the disjoint union $Y = \sum_j \oplus Y_j$ of all the Y_j's, and define the direct sum $k = \sum_j \oplus k_j$ on $X \times Y$ by

$$k(x, y) = \begin{cases} k_j(x, y) & \text{when } \langle x, y \rangle \in X_j \times Y_j, \\ 0 & \text{otherwise.} \end{cases}$$

Suppose, for example, that J is the set of positive integers, and that $X_j = Y_j = \{j\}$ for each j in J. Since $X_j \times Y_j$ is a singleton, a kernel k_j on $X_j \times Y_j$ is just a constant λ_j. The direct sum $\sum_j \oplus k_j$ becomes in this case the diagonal matrix

(1)
$$\begin{pmatrix} \lambda_1 & & & \\ & \lambda_2 & & \\ & & \lambda_3 & \\ & & & \ddots \end{pmatrix}.$$

For another example with the same J, suppose that $X_j = Y_j = \mathbb{I}$. A natural way to visualize the process of making the X_j's and the Y_j's disjoint is to think of them as having been translated by $j-1$ units forward in $\mathbb{R}_+$. (Overlapping end points should be ignored. In the applications of the theory they constitute a set of measure zero and contribute nothing to the operators induced by the kernels.) The direct unions $\sum_j \oplus X_j$ and $\sum_j \oplus Y_j$ then become $\mathbb{R}_+$, and the direct sum $\sum_j \oplus k_j$ of a family $\{k_j : j \in J\}$ of kernels becomes the kernel k indicated by the diagram:

(2)

(In both (1) and (2), entries not indicated are to be filled by 0's.)

Remark. ▶ Classical notational traditions force the curious 90° difference between (1) and (2). In matrices the first variable indicates horizontal sections (rows), but in kernels the first variable indicates vertical sections (columns). An infinite matrix is a function on $\mathbb{Z}_+ \times \mathbb{Z}_+$; pictorially, it starts at a point and moves down and right. A kernel on $\mathbb{R}_+ \times \mathbb{R}_+$, on the other hand, is usually pictured as starting at a point and moving right and up. To make a kernel picture out of a matrix picture, rotate it by 90° upward (in the mathematically positive direction). There is nothing wrong with any of this; it just takes a little getting used to. ◀

A useful way of making a new matrix out of two old ones is to form their *Kronecker product*: given a and a', let $a \otimes a'$ be the matrix, indexed by pairs of pairs $\langle\langle i, i'\rangle, \langle j, j'\rangle\rangle$, whose general entry is $a(i,j) a'(i',j')$. Pictorially: replace each entry $a(i,j)$ of a by the product of the scalar $a(i,j)$ and the matrix a'. Is there a useful generalization of this construction to all kernels? The question does not seem to have been studied much, and it is not clear how useful an answer could be. Formally the basic concept almost defines itself: given kernels k on $X \times Y$ and k' on $X' \times Y'$, define their *tensor product* to be the kernel $k \otimes k'$ on $(X \times X') \times (Y \times Y')$ given by

$$(k \otimes k')(\langle x, x'\rangle, \langle y, y'\rangle) = k(x,y) k'(x',y').$$

If, for instance, a is the infinite identity matrix, then $a \otimes k'$ is the direct sum of infinitely many copies of k'. Another example: if k' is the kernel on $\mathbb{I} \times \mathbb{I}$ defined by $k'(x,y) = 1$ for all x and y, and if a is an infinite matrix, then $a \otimes k'$ is the kernel on $\mathbb{R}_+ \times \mathbb{R}_+$ that takes the constant value $a(i,j)$ on the square $(i-1, i) \times (j-1, j)$. The latter construction is used often enough to deserve a name: the kernel it produces will be called the *inflation* of the original matrix. In pictures: the inflation of the matrix

$$\begin{pmatrix} k(0,0) & k(0,1) & k(0,2) \\ k(1,0) & k(1,1) & k(1,2) \\ k(2,0) & k(2,1) & k(2,2) \\ & & & \ddots \end{pmatrix}$$

is the kernel

$k(0,2)$	$k(1,2)$	$k(2,2)$	
$k(0,1)$	$k(1,1)$	$k(2,1)$	
$k(0,0)$	$k(1,0)$	$k(2,0)$	

that takes the indicated values in the indicated unit squares.[2]

The constructions discussed so far depend on the underlying *measurable* spaces but not on the numerical values of the *measures* on them. Because a kernel is, by definition, a measurable function, each construction should in principle be accompanied by a proof that its output is measurable; in practice the measurability proofs are easy exercises and their omission should cause no inconvenience.

The facts are different for the most important construction of them all, the matrix product. If a and a' are $n \times n$ matrices (rectangular matrices could be treated here too, but the only difference would be some notational complication), then their product is the matrix b defined by

$$b(i,j) = \sum_p a(i,p) a'(p,j).$$

The natural kernel generalization is the *convolution* of two kernels k and k'; it is the kernel h defined by

$$h(x,y) = \int k(x,z) k'(z,y) \, dz.$$

Trouble: the necessary integration may fail to be performable. The trouble is not just that some obvious integrability assumption has not yet been formulated; the trouble occurs with many otherwise well-behaved kernels and it is symptomatic of the basic difficulties of the entire theory.

Notational comment: integrals will usually be written with the classical differential symbolism (such as dx) instead of its slightly modernized and notationally more detailed versions (such as $d\mu(x)$). The measure that is being used will usually be obvious from the context; the only time it will be explicitly indicated is when more than one measure in the same space is under discussion. Integrals with no indicated domain, such as $\int k(x,y) g(y) \, dy$, are always to be extended over the entire space on which the integrands are defined.

§3. Domains

The way a matrix acts is defined by the familiar formula

(1) $$f(i)=\sum_j a(i,j)\, g(j).$$

The generalization to arbitrary kernels is formally obvious:

(2) $$f(x)=\int k(x,y)\, g(y)\, dy.$$

Finite sums such as the ones in (1) can always be formed; integrals such as the ones indicated in (2) may fail to exist and, even when they exist, may fail to define well-behaved functions.

For an unrestricted kernel k on $X \times Y$ the best that can be done is to study the largest possible set of functions g in L^2 for which (2) makes sense and yields a function f that is again in L^2. Precisely, the *domain* of a kernel k is the set

$$\operatorname{dom} k$$

of all those g in $L^2(Y)$ that satisfy the following two conditions:

$$k(x,\cdot)\,g\in L^1(Y) \quad \text{for almost every } x \text{ in } X,$$

and

$$\text{if } f(x)=\int k(x,y)\, g(y)\, dy, \quad \text{then } f\in L^2(X).$$

Explanation of notation:

$$k(x,\cdot)$$

is, for each fixed x, the function on Y defined by

$$k(x,\cdot)(y)=k(x,y).$$

(Similarly, of course, $k(\cdot,y)$ is, for each fixed y, the function on X defined by $k(\cdot,y)(x)=k(x,y)$.) The domain of every kernel is obviously a linear manifold in $L^2(Y)$. Since the mapping $g\mapsto f$ is equally obviously linear, the *range* of the kernel, i.e., the set

$$\operatorname{ran} k$$

of all f's in $L^2(X)$ obtainable by applying k to some g in $\operatorname{dom} k$, is a linear manifold in $L^2(X)$.

The discussion above implicitly took the usual analytic attitude, to be maintained throughout, according to which the elements of L^2 are functions, but equality means equivalence modulo sets of measure zero. In accordance with this attitude, all statements, whether they are set-theoretic ($E\subset F$), algebraic

$(f-g=0)$, or topological $(\lim_{n} f_n=0)$ are to be interpreted in the measure-theoretic, almost-everywhere, sense ($E-F$ has measure zero, f and g take the same values almost everywhere, $f_n(x)\to 0$ for almost every x). Incidentally, for subsets of and functions on measure spaces the qualification "measurable" is frequently omitted when the context permits; this is especially true in contexts such as "let E be a [measurable] set of positive measure".

What can the domain of a kernel be? If $k(x,y)$ is identically 0, then $\operatorname{dom} k = L^2(Y)$ (and $\operatorname{ran} k$ is the subspace 0 of $L^2(X)$): the domain of a kernel can be large. Can it be small?

Example 3.1. Is there a kernel k such that $\operatorname{dom} k=0$?

The answer is not obvious even for the special case of matrices. The attempt to construct a matrix with domain 0 is likely to begin by using "many" entries, as in

$$\begin{pmatrix} 1 & 1 & 1 & 1 \\ 1 & 1 & 1 & 1 \\ 1 & 1 & 1 & 1 \\ 1 & 1 & 1 & 1 \\ & & & & \ddots \end{pmatrix}.$$

No good: the vector g with $g(1)=1$, $g(2)=-1$, and $g(n)=0$ otherwise, is in the domain. How about "large" entries, as in

$$\begin{pmatrix} 1 & 2 & 3 & 4 \\ 0 & 1 & 2 & 3 \\ 0 & 0 & 1 & 2 \\ 0 & 0 & 0 & 1 \\ & & & & \ddots \end{pmatrix}?$$

No good: the vector g with $g(n)=\dfrac{1}{n^3}$ is in the domain.

▶ Perhaps the simplest example of a matrix with domain 0 is this:

$$\begin{pmatrix} 1 & 0 & 0 & 0 & 0 & 0 & 0 & 0 & 0 & 0 \\ 1 & 0 & 0 & 0 & 0 & 0 & 0 & 0 & 0 & 0 \\ 0 & 1 & 0 & 0 & 0 & 0 & 0 & 0 & 0 & 0 \\ 1 & 0 & 0 & 0 & 0 & 0 & 0 & 0 & 0 & 0 \\ 0 & 1 & 0 & 0 & 0 & 0 & 0 & 0 & 0 & 0 \\ 0 & 0 & 1 & 0 & 0 & 0 & 0 & 0 & 0 & 0 \\ 1 & 0 & 0 & 0 & 0 & 0 & 0 & 0 & 0 & 0 \\ 0 & 1 & 0 & 0 & 0 & 0 & 0 & 0 & 0 & 0 \\ 0 & 0 & 1 & 0 & 0 & 0 & 0 & 0 & 0 & 0 \\ 0 & 0 & 0 & 1 & 0 & 0 & 0 & 0 & 0 & 0 \\ & & & & & & & & & & \ddots \end{pmatrix}.$$

Each row has one 1 and the rest 0's; the 1's occur in the columns

$$1, 1, 2, 1, 2, 3, 1, 2, 3, 4, \ldots .$$

If g is an arbitrary vector, then the image of g contains each $g(n)$ infinitely often. Consequence: the image can be in ℓ^2 only if all the $g(n)$'s are equal to 0.

A modification of the technique yields a kernel with domain 0 on a divisible space. Let $\{(a_n, b_n): n = 1, 2, 3, \ldots\}$ be an enumeration of the rational intervals in $\mathbb{R}_+$ such that each one occurs infinitely often, and let k be the kernel on $\mathbb{R}_+ \times \mathbb{R}_+$ defined as follows:

$$k(x, y) = \begin{cases} 1 & \text{if } x \in (n, n+1) \text{ and } y \in (a_n, b_n), \\ 0 & \text{otherwise.} \end{cases}$$

Suppose now that $g \in L^2(\mathbb{R}_+)$. If $x \in (n, n+1)$, then

$$f(x) = \int k(x, y) g(y) \, dy = \int_{a_n}^{b_n} g(y) \, dy.$$

The only way the transform f can be in $L^2(\mathbb{R}_+)$ is to have $\int_{a_n}^{b_n} g(y) \, dy = 0$ for all n. (Reason: otherwise f takes a non-zero constant value on a set of infinite measure.) Consequence: the only way g can be in dom k is to have the integral of g vanish over every rational interval. It follows that if $g \in \text{dom } k$, then the indefinite integral of g is identically 0, and hence that $g = 0$ almost everywhere. ◄

Example 3.2. A kernel that plays a basic role in a nearby part of analysis (the kernel that defines the *Hilbert transform*) is defined on $\mathbb{R} \times \mathbb{R}$ by

$$k(x, y) = \frac{1}{x - y}.$$

(The diagonal $\{\langle x, y \rangle : x - y = 0\}$ is a set of measure 0 in the plane; the value of k on it is immaterial.) Assertion: dom $k = 0$.

▶ In fact: if g is a measurable function on $\mathbb{R}$ such that $k(x, \cdot) g \in L^1(\mathbb{R})$ for almost every x, then $g = 0$ almost everywhere. Assume, on the contrary, that $g \neq 0$ almost everywhere; then there exists a positive number δ such that $\{y : |g(y)| > \delta\}$ has positive measure. Change scale and assume (with no loss of generality) that there exists a set E of positive measure such that

$$\chi_E(y) \leq |g(y)|$$

for all y. (Here and throughout the letter χ is reserved for characteristic functions of sets.) It is therefore sufficient to prove that $k(x, \cdot) \chi_E$ cannot be in $L^1(R)$ for almost every x. If E is an interval, this is obvious. The proof in the general case depends on the fact that every set of positive measure is approximately an interval: in a neighborhood of each point of density it fills most of an interval. What the proof shows is that, in fact, if x is a point of density of E, then $k(x,\cdot)\chi_E\notin L^1$.[3]

If x is a point of density of E, then

$$\frac{1}{2\varepsilon}\mu((x-\varepsilon,x+\varepsilon)\cap E)\to 1$$

as $\varepsilon\to 0$, so that

$$\mu((x-\varepsilon,x+\varepsilon)\cap E)\geq\varepsilon$$

for ε sufficiently small. It follows that

$$\int_{x-\varepsilon}^{x+\varepsilon}\frac{\chi_E(y)}{|x-y|}\,dy\geq\frac{1}{\varepsilon}\cdot\varepsilon$$

for all sufficiently small ε. This, however, is incompatible with $k(x,\cdot)\chi_E\in L^1(\mathbb{R})$: if that were true, then the integral would tend to 0 as $\varepsilon\to 0$. ◄

If the measure spaces X and Y are "small" (i.e., if they have only a finite number of points), then the domain of a kernel on $X\times Y$ is necessarily "full" (i.e., equal to $L^2(Y)$); if, however, $L^2(Y)$ is infinite-dimensional, then the domain of a kernel may be extremely small (i.e., equal to 0). It is easy to form direct sums of such extreme examples to get kernels whose domains are subspaces (closed linear manifolds) in $L^2(Y)$; Example 3.11, however, shows that not every kernel with closed domain can be obtained that way.

Problem 3.3. ► *What are all kernels with closed domain?* ◄

Even a quick introduction to the subject of domains should not conclude without pointing out that some of them may fail to be closed.

Example 3.4. ► If $a=\text{diag}(0,1,2,3,\ldots)$, i.e., $a(i,j)=i\delta(i,j)$ for all i and j in $\mathbb{Z}_+$ (where δ is the Kronecker symbol, the characteristic function of the diagonal in $\mathbb{Z}_+\times\mathbb{Z}_+$), then $\text{dom}\,a$ is the set of all vectors g in ℓ^2 for which $\sum_n n^2|g(n)|^2<\infty$; that set is dense in ℓ^2. ◄

Example 3.5. ► If $a(i,j)=1$ for all i and j in $\mathbb{Z}_+$, then $\text{dom}\,a$ is the set of all those vectors g in ℓ^2 for which $g\in\ell^1$ and $\sum_n g(n)=0$; that set too is dense in ℓ^2.

(Reason: if g is a finitely non-zero vector and m is a positive integer, write $\gamma=\sum_n g(n)$, and let g' be the vector that agrees with g up to and including the last place where g has a non-zero value and then continues with m values each equal to $-\gamma/m$. It follows that $g'\in\ell^1$, $\sum_n g'(n)=0$, and

$$\|g-g'\|_2=\sqrt{m\cdot|\gamma|^2/m^2}=|\gamma|/\sqrt{m};$$

the latter becomes arbitrarily small as m increases.) ◄

12

In any event, whatever its domain might be, a kernel always induces an operator, to be denoted by

$$\text{Int } k,$$

that maps dom k (in $L^2(Y)$) into $L^2(X)$; the image under Int k of a function g in dom k is, of course, the function f in $L^2(X)$ given (as in (2)) by

$$f(x) = \int k(x, y)\, g(y)\, dy.$$

The *integral operator* Int k is linear, of course, but not necessarily bounded. It may fail to possess other pleasant analytic properties also; it may, for instance, fail to be closed. While this book is devoted to the study of bounded integral operators, and the question whether certain unbounded operators are closed is largely beside the point, a couple of simple examples (certain integral operators are not closed) and a couple of basic theorems (certain integral operators are closed) shed some light on the delicacy of the theory as a whole; here they are.

Example 3.6. If X is a one-point space, $X = \mathbb{Z}_1$, say, and $Y = \mathbb{Z}_+$, and the kernel k on $X \times Y$ is defined by

$$k(1, n) = n + 1, \qquad n = 0, 1, 2, 3, \ldots,$$

then Int k is not closed.[4]

▶ When is a sequence g in $L^2(Y)$ an element of dom k? For that to happen it is necessary that $k(1, \cdot) g \in L^1(Y)$, so that $\sum_n (n+1)|g(n)| < \infty$; in view of the triviality of the space X, the condition is sufficient also. If, in particular, $g_m = \frac{1}{m+1}\chi_m$ (where χ_m is the characteristic function of $\{m\}$ in Y), then $g_m \in \text{dom } k$ and

$$(\text{Int } k)\, g_m(1) = \sum_n (n+1)\, g_m(n) = 1.$$

Since $\|g_m\| = \frac{1}{m+1} \to 0$, the sequence $\{\langle g_m, 1\rangle\}$ in the graph of Int k converges to $\langle 0, 1\rangle$, which cannot be in the graph of anything. The operator Int k is not only not closed, it is not even closeable. ◀

The preceding example smacks of pathology, but there are others that are completely in the spirit of classical analysis.

Example 3.7. If $X = Y = \mathbb{I}$ and $k(x, y) = \frac{1}{y}$, then Int k is not closed.

▶ If $g_n(y) = \frac{1}{n} y^{1/n}$, then

$$\|g_n\|^2 = \frac{1}{n^2}\int_0^1 y^{2/n}\, dy = \frac{1}{n^2}\left[\frac{y^{1+2/n}}{1+2/n}\right]_0^1 = \frac{1}{2n+n^2} \to 0$$

and

$$\int_0^1 k(x,y)\,g_n(y)\,dy = \frac{1}{n}\int_0^1 y^{(1/n)-1}\,dy = \frac{1}{n}\left[\frac{y^{1/n}}{1/n}\right]_0^1 = 1. \quad \blacktriangleleft$$

Sometimes positive kernels (i.e., $k(x,y)\geq 0$ for almost every $\langle x,y\rangle$) behave better than others; as the preceding examples show, however, in the consideration of closedness positivity is no help.

A class of kernels that is both historically and conceptually important bears the name of Carleman; a *Carleman kernel* k is, by definition, one for which

$$k(x,\cdot)\in L^2(Y)$$

for almost every x in X. For Carleman kernels part of the definition of domain can be omitted (because it is automatically satisfied): if k is a Carleman kernel, and if $g\in L^2(Y)$, then $k(x,\cdot)\,g\in L^1(Y)$ for almost every x (because every function in L^2 multiplies L^2 into L^1). For such kernels, therefore, the domain consists of those functions g in $L^2(Y)$ whose transform (unambiguously defined for almost every x in X) belongs to $L^2(X)$.[5]

Theorem 3.8. *If k is a Carleman kernel, then* Int k *is closed.*

▶ Suppose that $g_n\in\mathrm{dom}\,k$, $f_n=(\mathrm{Int}\,k)\,g_n$, $g_n\to g$ (in $L^2(Y)$), and $f_n\to f$ (in $L^2(X)$); it is to be proved that $g\in\mathrm{dom}\,k$ and $(\mathrm{Int}\,k)\,g=f$. Since $g_n\to g$ weakly, it follows that $(k(x,\cdot),\bar g_n)\to(k(x,\cdot),\bar g)$ whenever $k(x,\cdot)\in L^2(Y)$, and hence that $f_n(x)\to\int k(x,y)\,g(y)\,dy$ for almost every x. Since, however, a subsequence of $\{f_n\}$ converges to f almost everywhere, it follows that $\int k(x,y)\,g(y)\,dy=f(x)$ almost everywhere. ◀

The closed graph theorem (for linear transformations between Banach spaces) says that if both the domain and the graph are closed, then the transformation is necessarily continuous. The next principal result (Theorem 3.10) about integral operators is sharper (no assumptions on the graph), and its proof is more subtle than a brutal application of the closed graph theorem. In case $X=\mathbb{Z}$, the assertion is that "an everywhere defined matrix is bounded". The proof is an application of Theorem 3.8 (and, to be sure, of the closed graph theorem). Indeed: if $k(n,\cdot)\,g\in L^1(Y)$ for all n in $\mathbb{Z}$ whenever $g\in L^2(Y)$, i.e., if each function $k(n,\cdot)$ multiplies $L^2(Y)$ into $L^1(Y)$, then, by a well-known pretty fact of analysis, each function $k(n,\cdot)$ belongs to $L^2(Y)$. In other words, k is a Carleman kernel; by Theorem 3.8, Int k is closed, and the closed graph theorem implies that k is bounded. In the general case, the main tool in the proof is a measure-theoretic lemma that does not usually receive any emphasis; it does not seem to be in the conscious memory of even the experts.

Lemma 3.9. *Every sequence that converges in $L^2(Y)$ has a dominated subsequence that converges almost everywhere.*

▶ The important word is "dominated". That is: if $g_n\to g$ in $L^2(Y)$, then there is an increasing sequence $\{n_j\}$ of positive integers, and there is a positive function h

in $L^2(Y)$ such that $g_{n_j}(y) \to g(y)$ and $|g_{n_j}(y)| \leq h(y)$ for almost every y. The result does not seem to follow from the Riesz-Fischer theorem, but is implicit in the usual proof of that theorem.

Find $\{n_j\}$ so that

$$\sum_{j=1}^{\infty} \|g_{n_{j+1}} - g_{n_j}\| < \infty.$$

For typographical convenience, change the notation: replace n_j by n, i.e., assume that

$$\sum_{n=1}^{\infty} \|g_{n+1} - g_n\| < \infty,$$

and, for notational simplicity, define $g_0 = 0$. Consider now the infinite series

$$h = \sum_{n=0}^{\infty} |g_{n+1} - g_n|,$$

with partial sums

$$h_j = \sum_{n=0}^{j} |g_{n+1} - g_n|.$$

Since

$$\int |h_j|^2 \, dv = \|h_j\|^2 = \left\| \sum_{n=0}^{j} |g_{n+1} - g_n| \right\|^2$$

$$\leq \left(\sum_{n=0}^{j} \|g_{n+1} - g_n\| \right)^2 \leq \left(\sum_{n=0}^{\infty} \|g_{n+1} - g_n\| \right)^2,$$

it follows that $h^2 \in L^1(Y)$, and hence that $h \in L^2(Y)$. Since, therefore, the series $\sum_{n=0}^{\infty} (g_{n+1} - g_n)$ is absolutely convergent almost everywhere, with partial sums

$$\sum_{n=0}^{j} (g_{n+1} - g_n) = g_{j+1},$$

and since

$$|g_{j+1}| \leq \sum_{n=0}^{j} |g_{n+1} - g_n| \leq h,$$

the proof of the lemma is complete. ◀

Theorem 3.10. *If a kernel k is such that* $\text{dom } k = L^2(Y)$ *then* $\text{Int } k$ *is bounded.*[6]

▶ Write $\text{Int } k = A$. To make the closed graph theorem applicable, it is to be proved that if $\langle g_n, f_n \rangle \in \text{graph } A$, i.e., $f_n = A g_n$, $n = 1, 2, 3, \ldots$, and if $f_n \to f$ in $L^2(X)$ and $g_n \to g$ in $L^2(Y)$, then $Ag = f$. By dropping down to subsequences (twice if necessary), assume that

$$f_n \to f, \quad g_n \to g, \quad \text{and} \quad |g_n| \leq h$$

almost everywhere for some h in $L^2(X)$ (Lemma 3.9). It follows that, for almost every x,

$$k(x, y) g_n(y) \to k(x, y) g(y)$$

and

$$|k(x, y) g_n(y)| \leq |k(x, y)| \cdot h(y)$$

for almost every y. That is: for almost every x, the sequence $\{k(x, \cdot) g_n\}$ in $L^1(Y)$ converges to $k(x, \cdot) g$ dominatedly almost everywhere. Note that since $h \in L^2(Y)$, the dominant functions $|k(x, \cdot)| \cdot h$ belong to $L^1(Y)$. Consequence: not only is $k(x, \cdot) g$ in $L^1(Y)$, but also

$$\int k(x, y) g_n(y) \, dy \to \int k(x, y) g(y) \, dy$$

for almost every x. That is:

$$f_n(x) \to \int k(x, y) g(y) \, dy$$

for almost every x. Since $f_n \to f$ in $L^2(X)$, it follows that

$$f(x) = \int k(x, y) g(y) \, dy$$

for almost every x; this completes the proof that A is closed. The boundedness of A is a consequence of the closed graph theorem. ◄

The main condition that a function g on Y must satisfy in order that it belong to the domain of a kernel k is that the transform f, defined by

$$f(x) = \int k(x, y) g(y) \, dy,$$

be square integrable. In order for that to make sense it is, of course, necessary to require also that the transform exist, i.e., that $k(x, \cdot) g$ be integrable for almost every x. Theorem 3.10 says that if both conditions are satisfied for every g in $L^2(Y)$, then k is bounded. What if only the first condition is satisfied for every g in $L^2(Y)$: does it still follow that k is bounded? Equivalently: does the existence of the transform imply its square integrability? The answer is no.

Example 3.11. ► Let u be a measurable function on X that is *not* in $L^2(X)$, let v be in $L^2(Y)$, and write

$$k(x, y) = u(x) \overline{v(y)}.$$

Since $k(x, \cdot) \in L^2(Y)$ for every x, it follows that $k(x, \cdot) g \in L^1(Y)$ for all g in $L^2(Y)$; the integrability condition is satisfied by all g. Since, however,

$$\int k(x, y) g(y) \, dy = u(x) \int \overline{v(y)} g(y) \, dy,$$

so that the transform of every g is a scalar multiple of u, it follows that if g is not orthogonal to v, then the transform of g is not square integrable. ◄

Problem 3.12. ▶ What Theorem 3.10 really proves is that if the domain of a kernel is the whole space $L^2(Y)$, then the induced integral operator is necessarily closed. What can be said about a kernel whose domain is closed (but not necessarily equal to the whole space)? (Cf. Problem 3.3.) *Is the induced integral operator always closed?* The answer is not known, not even in the possibly simpler cases (a) where the kernel is positive, and (b) where the underlying spaces are atomic. ◀

An examination of the proofs of Lemma 3.9 and Theorem 3.10 shows that if dom k is closed and if, moreover, dom k is closed under the formation of absolute values (i.e., if $g \in$ dom k always implies $|g| \in$ dom k), then the argument works: the induced integral operator is necessarily closed. (The dominant, h, belongs to the span of the absolute values $|g_{n+1} - g_n|$; what is wanted is that it belong to dom k.) This kind of "absolute closure" may, however, be more than is needed. It is, by the way, easy enough to construct an example of a kernel whose domain is not closed under the formation of absolute values. The matrix

$$k = \begin{pmatrix} 1 & 1 & & & & & \\ 1 & 1 & & & & & \\ & & 2 & 2 & & & \\ & & 2 & 2 & & & \\ & & & & 3 & 3 & \\ & & & & 3 & 3 & \\ & & & & & & \ddots \end{pmatrix}$$

is such an example. Indeed, $g \in$ dom k if and only if

$$\sum_n n^2 \, |g(2n-1)+g(2n)|^2 < \infty;$$

the sequence $g = \{1, -1, \frac{1}{2}, -\frac{1}{2}, \frac{1}{3}, -\frac{1}{3}, ...\}$ satisfies the condition, but $|g|$ does not. This is, however, not a counter-example to the statement "closed domain implies closed operator", i.e., it is not an example of a non-closed integral operator with closed domain, for two reasons: the operator is closed and the domain is not.

§4. Boundedness

Since most of the work that follows concerns kernels k for which $\operatorname{dom} k = L^2(Y)$ (and, for which, therefore, Int k is bounded – see Theorem 3.10), it is convenient to have a short word to describe such kernels; the commonly accepted word is *bounded*. Generalizations of this verbal convention are often convenient. The idea is to use for a kernel words and symbols that properly speaking are associated with the induced operator. Example: $\operatorname{dom} k$ is in reality the domain of Int k. Another possibility: a kernel may or may not be closed. (Problem 3.12 can therefore be expressed this way: is it true that if $\operatorname{dom} k$ is closed, then k is closed?) A notational possibility for bounded kernels (that is hereby adopted): write $\|k\|$ instead of $\|\operatorname{Int} k\|$.

Caution: to say of a kernel k that it is bounded in the sense defined above is far from saying that the function k is pointwise bounded on $X \times Y$ (everywhere, or almost everywhere); for operator boundedness the condition of pointwise boundedness is both unneccessary and insufficient.

Counterexamples in one direction are easy to find: two of the three matrices mentioned in Example 3.1 (e.g., $a(i, j) = 1$ for all i and j) are bounded as functions but not bounded as operators, and the same is true of their inflations to $\mathbb{R}_+ \times \mathbb{R}_+$. It is not a coincidence that the measures in these examples are infinite. If the measures in X and Y are finite, then every pointwise bounded measurable function on $X \times Y$ turns out to be a bounded kernel (this will be proved presently), but, even for finite measures, pointwise boundedness is not necessary for operator boundedness.

Lemma 4.1. *If $k \in L^2(X \times Y)$ (with respect to the product measure $\mu \otimes \nu$), then k is a bounded kernel, and, in fact,*

$$\|k\| \leq \|k\|_2,$$

where $\|k\|_2$ is the norm of k in $L^2(X \times Y)$.

▶ The proof is a straightforward application of the Schwarz inequality. Indeed, if $g \in L^2(Y)$, then

$$\int |\int k(x, y) g(y) \, dy|^2 \, dx \leq \int (\int |k(x, y)|^2 \, dy)(\int |g(y)|^2 \, dy) \, dx$$
$$= \|k\|_2^2 \cdot \|g\|^2. \quad ◀$$

The integral operator induced by a kernel in $L^2(X \times Y)$ is called a *Hilbert-Schmidt operator;* these operators became important early in the history of the subject, and still are. [7] The norm $\|k\|_2$ is sometimes called the *Hilbert-Schmidt norm* of the kernel k.

Example 4.2. ▶ If u and v are square integrable (but not necessarily bounded) functions in $L^2(X)$ and $L^2(Y)$ respectively, then their *tensor product* $u \otimes v$, defined by

$$(u \otimes v)(x, y) = u(x)\, \overline{v(y)},$$

is a square integrable (but not necessarily bounded) function in $L^2(X \times Y)$. (The complex conjugate in the definition of $u \otimes v$ is not important, but it is convenient. It is bound to come in somewhere, and some later formulas will be simpler if it is allowed here.) Consequence: the kernel k is bounded (but not necessarily pointwise bounded).

If the measures μ and ν are finite, then every pointwise bounded measurable function is square integrable, and, therefore, is a bounded kernel on $X \times Y$, which induces a Hilbert-Schmidt operator.

A trivial but interesting special case is given by

$$k(x, y) = 1 \quad \text{for all } x \text{ and } y.$$

A classically important special case (with $X = Y = \mathbb{I}$) is given by

$$k(x, y) = \begin{cases} 0 & \text{for } x \leq y, \\ 1 & \text{for } x > y. \end{cases}$$

The operator $V = \text{Int}\, k$ induced by this kernel is called the *Volterra* operator; for each g in L^2, the image Vg is the indefinite integral of g. ◀

Hilbert-Schmidt operators are useful not only as examples; a large part of the classical theory of integral equations is based on them. What follows is a brief discussion of their most important properties.

Lemma 4.3. *If u and v are non-zero elements of $L^2(X)$ and $L^2(Y)$ respectively and $k = u \otimes v$ (i.e., $k(x, y) = u(x)\, \overline{v(y)}$), then the Hilbert-Schmidt operator $\text{Int}\, k$ has rank 1; if, conversely, A is an arbitrary bounded operator from $L^2(Y)$ to $L^2(X)$ with rank 1, then $A = \text{Int}\, k$ for some kernel k of the form $u \otimes v$.*

▶ Since $(\text{Int}\, k)\, g(x) = \int u(x)\, \overline{v(y)}\, g(y)\, dy = (g, v)\, u(x)$, it is clear that every vector in the range of $\text{Int}\, k$ is a scalar multiple of u. If, conversely, A is an operator of rank 1, let u be a non-zero element in the range of A. It follows that Ag is a multiple of u for every g in $L^2(Y)$, where the multiplier depends on g, of course, and does so in a bounded linear manner. Consequence: $Ag = (g, v)u$ for some v in $L^2(Y)$. Conclusion:

$$A\, g(x) = \int u(x)\, \overline{v(y)}\, g(y)\, dy,$$

or, in other words, $A = \text{Int}\, k$ with $k = u \otimes v$. ◀

Corollary 4.4. *If* $u_1, \ldots, u_n$ *are in* $L^2(X)$, $v_1, \ldots, v_n$ *are in* $L^2(Y)$, *and* $k = \sum_{j=1}^{n} u_j \otimes v_j$, *then* rank Int $k \leq n$. *If, conversely,* A *is an arbitrary bounded operator from* $L^2(Y)$ *to* $L^2(X)$ *with* rank $A \leq n$, *then* $A = $ Int k *for some kernel* k *of the form* $\sum_{j=1}^{n} u_j \otimes v_j$.

The extension of the finite sums in Corollary 4.4 to infinite ones is the backbone of the whole Hilbert-Schmidt theory.

Theorem 4.5. *If* A *is a Hilbert-Schmidt operator from* $L^2(Y)$ *to* $L^2(X)$ *and* $\{g_j\}$ *is an orthonormal set in* $L^2(Y)$, *then* $\sum_j \|A g_j\|^2 < \infty$. *If, conversely, a bounded linear operator* A *from* $L^2(Y)$ *to* $L^2(X)$ *is such that* $\sum_j \|A g_j\|^2 < \infty$ *for some orthonormal basis* $\{g_j\}$ *in* $L^2(Y)$, *then* A *is a Hilbert-Schmidt operator.*

▶ If $\{f_i\}$ and $\{g_j\}$ are orthonormal bases in $L^2(X)$ and $L^2(Y)$ respectively, then the vectors $f_i \otimes g_j$ form an orthonormal basis for $L^2(X \times Y)$. (Reason: tensor products of the form $f \otimes g$, where f and g are finite linear combinations of the f_i and of the g_j, respectively, are dense in the set of all tensor products $u \otimes v$; finite linear combinations of tensor products $u \otimes v$ are, by the very definition of product measure, dense in $L^2(X \times Y)$.) It follows that if A is an arbitrary bounded linear operator from $L^2(Y)$ to $L^2(X)$, then (by the Parseval identity)

$$(1) \qquad \sum_j \|A g_j\|^2 = \sum_i \sum_j |(A g_j, f_i)|^2.$$

If, on the other hand, $k \in L^2(X \times Y)$, then

$$(2) \qquad (k, f_i \otimes g_j) = \iint k(x, y) \overline{f_i(x)} g_j(y) \, dx \, dy$$
$$= \int (\int k(x, y) g_j(y) \, dy) \overline{f_i(x)} \, dx = ((\text{Int } k) g_j, f_i).$$

Both assertions of the theorem are consequences of the equations (1) and (2); the reasoning goes like this.

If $A = $ Int k, with k in $L^2(X \times Y)$, then, by (2), the right side of (1) is finite (because it is equal to $\|k\|_2^2$), and, therefore, so is the left, no matter which orthonormal basis $\{g_j\}$ is used.

If the left side of (1) is finite for some $\{g_j\}$, then so is the right, and, therefore,

$$\sum_i \sum_j (A g_j, f_i)(f_i \otimes g_j)$$

converges in $L^2(X \times Y)$ to some element k of $L^2(X \times Y)$, with Fourier coefficients $(k, f_i \otimes g_j) = (A g_j, f_i)$; this and (2) imply that $A = $ Int k. ◀

Corollary 4.6. *Every Hilbert-Schmidt operator is compact.*

▶ If $A = $ Int k, as above, then the Fourier expansion

$$k = \sum_i \sum_j (k, f_i \otimes g_j)(f_i \otimes g_j)$$

shows that k is the L^2 limit of finite sums of tensor products. The inequality in Lemma 4.1 implies that A is the norm limit of the integral operators induced by those finite sums; since they have finite ranks (Corollary 4.4), the conclusion follows. ◄

Corollary 4.7. *A bounded linear operator A from $L^2(Y)$ to $L^2(X)$ is a Hilbert-Schmidt operator if and only if it is compact and the sum of the squares of the eigenvalues of $\sqrt{A^*A}$ (with multiplicities counted) is finite.*

▶ If A is an operator from $L^2(Y)$ to $L^2(X)$, if $\{\lambda_j\}$ is a family of scalars, and if $\{g_j\}$ is a corresponding orthonormal basis for $L^2(Y)$ such that

$$\sqrt{A^*A}\,g_j = \lambda_j g_j,$$

then

(3) $$\sum_j \lambda_j^2 = \sum_j (A^*A\,g_j, g_j) = \sum_j \|A\,g_j\|^2.$$

If A is a Hilbert-Schmidt operator, then $\sqrt{A^*A}$, being Hermitian and compact, has an orthonormal basis of eigenvectors; (3) and Theorem 4.5 together imply that the sum of the squares of the eigenvalues is finite. If, conversely, $\sqrt{A^*A}$ is compact and the sum of the squares of its eigenvalues is finite, then (3) and Theorem 4.5 together imply that A is a Hilbert-Schmidt operator. [Note that not every compact operator is a Hilbert-Schmidt operator; in fact, the class of Hilbert-Schmidt operators plays the same role in the class of compact operators as ℓ^2 plays in the space c_0 of null-convergent sequences. If $\lambda_j \to 0$, then A is compact, but A is not a Hilbert-Schmidt operator unless $\sum_j \lambda_j^2 < \infty$.]

Hilbert-Schmidt operators serve as sources of examples of bounded kernels that are not pointwise bounded, but they are important for many other much more powerful reasons, and are continually referred to in the theory of integral operators. The presence or absence of pointwise boundedness, on the other hand, is usually an unimportant side issue as far as integral operators are concerned. The issue can be interesting, nevertheless, and Example 4.2 is far from the last word on the subject. Some additional results about it (and a curious unsolved problem) can be found in Appendix B.

§5. Examples

The easiest examples of bounded kernels are the square-integrable ones introduced in Lemma 4.1; they induce Hilbert-Schmidt operators. The examples that follow are different; they are, for one thing, not compact.

Example 5.1. If $X = Y = \mathbb{R}_+$ and if

$$k(x, y) = \begin{cases} 1 & \text{for } n \leq x, \ y < n+1, \ n = 0, 1, 2, \ldots, \\ 0 & \text{otherwise} \end{cases}$$

then k is a bounded kernel; the induced integral operator is a projection with infinite rank and infinite nullity. Note that k is the inflation (in the sense of §2) of the identity matrix.

▶ The kernel k is not square integrable; it is, however, a Carleman kernel. If $g \in L^2$ and if χ_n is the characteristic function of $[n, n+1)$, then

$$\int k(x, y) g(y) \, dy = \sum_{n=0}^{\infty} \left(\int_n^{n+1} g(y) \, dy \right) \chi_n(x).$$

Since the functions $\chi_1, \chi_2, \ldots$ form an orthogonal set, it follows that

$$\int |\int k(x, y) g(y) \, dy|^2 \, dx = \sum_{n=0}^{\infty} \left| \int_n^{n+1} g(y) \, dy \right|^2$$

$$\leq \sum_{n=0}^{\infty} \int_n^{n+1} |g(y)|^2 \, dy = \|g\|^2,$$

which proves that k is bounded.

Observe that if $k_0(x, y) = 1$ on $\mathbb{I} \times \mathbb{I}$, then $\text{Int } k_0$ is a projection of rank 1. (Indeed: if $g \in L^2(\mathbb{I})$, then the transform of g is $(g, e)e$, where e is the constant function 1 on $\mathbb{I}$.) The kernel k is the direct sum of countably many copies of k_0, and, correspondingly, $\text{Int } k$ is the direct sum of countably many copies of $\text{Int } k_0$. That is to say, there is a theorem (9.1) about direct sums that says as much. Since that theorem is not yet on record here, its present application has to be verified separately. What is being asserted is that $\text{Int } k$ is idempotent and self-adjoint; both assertions follow from the expression for $(\text{Int } k) g$ in terms of the χ_n's. The functions χ_n form an orthonormal basis for the range of $\text{Int } k$. ◀

The theory of bounded kernels resembles the theory of convergent series in several respects. There is, for one thing, no usable necessary and sufficient condition for the boundedness of a kernel, just as there is none for the covergence of a series. The following sufficient condition (known as the *Schur test*) is often useful.

Theorem 5.2. *If k is a non-negative kernel, if p and q are strictly positive measurable functions on X and Y respectively, and if α and β are positive numbers such that*

$$\int k(x, y) q(y) \, dy \leq \alpha p(x) \quad \text{for almost every } x$$

and

$$\int k(x, y) p(x) \, dx \leq \beta q(y) \quad \text{for almost every } y,$$

then k is a bounded kernel and

$$\|k\|^2 \leq \alpha \beta.$$ [8]

▶ If g is an arbitrary element of $L^2(Y)$, then

$$\int \left(\int k(x, y)|g(y)| dy \right)^2 dx = \int \left(\int \sqrt{k(x, y)} \sqrt{q(y)} \left(\sqrt{\frac{k(x, y)}{q(y)}} |g(y)| \right) dy \right)^2 dx$$

$$\leq \int \left(\int k(x, y) q(y) \, dy \right) \left(\int \frac{k(x, y)}{q(y)} |g(y)|^2 \, dy \right) dx$$

$$\leq \int \alpha p(x) \int \frac{k(x, y)}{q(y)} |g(y)|^2 \, dy \, dx$$

$$= \alpha \int \frac{|g(y)|^2}{q(y)} \left(\int k(x, y) p(x) \, dx \right) dy$$

$$\leq \alpha \int \frac{|g(y)|^2}{q(y)} \beta q(y) \, dy = \alpha \beta \int |g(y)|^2 \, dy. \quad ◀$$

Example 5.3. If $X = Y = \mathbb{I}$, and if

$$k(x, y) = \begin{cases} 0 & \text{for } x \leq y, \\[2mm] \dfrac{1}{\sqrt{x-y}} & \text{for } x > y, \end{cases}$$

then k is a bounded kernel. Abel studied this kernel in his work on the vibrating string.

▶ The result is not at all obvious by inspection. An efficient way to prove it is to note that the two integrals

$$\int k(x, y) \, dy \quad \text{and} \quad \int k(x, y) \, dx$$

are bounded. The verification of that assertion is elementary calculus:

$$\int_0^x \frac{dy}{\sqrt{x-y}} = \int_0^1 \frac{x\,du}{\sqrt{x(1-u)}} \qquad (\text{put } y=ux)$$

$$= 2\sqrt{x} \leqq 2$$

and

$$\int_y^1 \frac{dx}{\sqrt{x-y}} = \int_1^{1/y} \frac{y\,du}{\sqrt{y(u-1)}} \qquad (\text{put } x=uy)$$

$$= 2\sqrt{1-y} \leqq 2.$$

With that the work is done: the Schur test is applicable with $p(x)=q(y)=1$ for all x and y and $\alpha=\beta=2$. ◀

Example 5.4. If $X=Y=\mathbb{R}_+$ and if

$$k(x, y) = \begin{cases} 0 & \text{for } x\leqq y, \\ \dfrac{1}{x} & \text{for } x>y, \end{cases}$$

then k is a bounded kernel. The operator Int k forms the "partial averages" of the functions in its domain, in this sense: if $g \in L^2$, then

$$(\text{Int } k)\,g(x) = \frac{1}{x} \int_0^x g(y)\,dy.$$

The right side of this equation is a "continuous" analogue of the formation of the Cesàro averages of a sequence.

▶ The simple form of the Schur test ($p=q=1$) does not work. The integral $\int_0^x \frac{1}{x}\,dy$ is, to be sure, bounded (as a function of x), but the integral $\int_y^\infty \frac{1}{x}\,dx$ is (as a function of y) not even finite. The way to find suitable functions p and q is by trial and error and luck. In the present case $p(x)=\dfrac{1}{\sqrt{x}}$, $q(y)=\dfrac{1}{\sqrt{y}}$ do the trick. Indeed:

$$\frac{1}{x} \int_0^x \frac{dy}{\sqrt{y}} = \frac{2}{\sqrt{x}},$$

and

$$\int_y^\infty \frac{dx}{x^{3/2}} = \frac{2}{\sqrt{y}}. \quad ◀$$

Example 5.5. If $X=Y=\mathbb{Z}_+$ and if $k(i,j)=\dfrac{1}{i+j+1}$ for $i,j=0,1,2,\ldots$, then k is a bounded kernel. The matrix k is one of two known as "the Hilbert matrix". Since matrices k for which

$$k(i,j)=k(i+1,j-1)$$

are called *Hankel matrices*, this Hilbert matrix might well be called the *Hilbert-Hankel matrix*.

▶ The Schur test is applicable again: write $p(i)=q(i)=\dfrac{1}{\sqrt{i+\frac{1}{2}}}$. Since k is symmetric, the two needed inequalities collapse into one. The verification is, again, elementary calculus, as follows:

$$\sum_i k(i,j)\,q(i)=\sum_i \frac{1}{(i+\frac{1}{2}+j+\frac{1}{2})\sqrt{i+\frac{1}{2}}}$$

$$< \int_0^\infty \frac{dx}{(x+j+\frac{1}{2})\sqrt{x}}=2\int_0^\infty \frac{du}{u^2+j+\frac{1}{2}}$$

$$=\frac{2}{\sqrt{j+\frac{1}{2}}}\int_0^\infty \frac{du}{u^2+1}=\frac{\pi}{\sqrt{j+\frac{1}{2}}}. \quad ◀$$

An analytically rich class of kernels is the class of Toeplitz matrices; they are the ones of the form

$$\begin{pmatrix} \alpha_0 & \alpha_{-1} & \alpha_{-2} & \\ \alpha_1 & \alpha_0 & \alpha_{-1} & \\ \alpha_2 & \alpha_1 & \alpha_0 & \\ & & & \ddots \end{pmatrix}.$$

In other words, a *Toeplitz matrix* k is determined by a two-sided infinite sequence $\{\alpha_n: n=0,\pm 1,\pm 2,\ldots\}$ by

$$k(i,j)=\alpha_{i-j}, \qquad i,j=0,1,2,\ldots.$$

The extensive theory of Toeplitz matrices includes, in particular, a surprisingly simple and usable answer to the question of when they are bounded. The statement is as follows.

Theorem 5.6. *If $\{\alpha_n\}$ is the sequence of Fourier coefficients of a function φ in $L^\infty(\mathbb{II})$ (with respect to the orthonormal basis for $L^2(\mathbb{II})$ defined by $e_n(x)=e^{2\pi inx}$, $n=0,\pm 1, \pm 2,\ldots$), then the Toeplitz matrix k_φ defined by $k_\varphi(i,j)=\alpha_{i-j}$ is bounded. If, conversely, k is a bounded Toeplitz matrix, and if $\alpha_n=k(n,0)$ or $k(0,-n)$ according as $n\geq 0$ or $n<0$, then $\{\alpha_n\}$ is the sequence of Fourier coefficients of a bounded measurable function.*

▶ The proof is omitted. It is not difficult, but its discussion here would be a digression from the sort of concepts and methods that are pertinent to the theory of integral operators. ◀ [9]

(Caution: the statement of Theorem 5.6 skirts close to an alphabetic collision: the letter "i" is used for both an integer index and $\sqrt{-1}$.)

Example 5.7. If $X = Y = \mathbb{Z}_+$, and if

$$k(i,j) = \begin{cases} \dfrac{1}{i-j} & \text{for } i,j = 0, 1, 2, \ldots, \\[2mm] 0 & \text{for } i = j, \end{cases}$$

then k is a bounded kernel. The matrix k is one of two known as "the Hilbert matrix". To distinguish it from the *Hilbert-Hankel matrix* (Example 5.5), this one might well be called the *Hilbert-Toeplitz matrix*. Note that it is skew-symmetric, so that multiplication by $\sqrt{-1}$ will make it Hermitian.

▶ Clearly k is a Toeplitz matrix: if $\alpha_0 = 0$ and $\alpha_n = 1/n$ when $n = \pm 1, \pm 2, \ldots$, then $k(i,j) = \alpha_{i-j}$. Since $\sum_n |\alpha_n|^2 < \infty$, the α_n's are the Fourier coefficients of a function φ in $L^2(0,1)$. The function φ is given by

$$\varphi(x) = \sum_{n \neq 0} \frac{1}{n} e^{2\pi i n x},$$

where the series converges at least in the L^2 sense. An elementary calculation reveals that

$$\varphi(x) = -2\pi i (x - \tfrac{1}{2})$$

almost everywhere. Since φ is bounded, it follows that the Hilbert matrix

$$\begin{pmatrix} 0 & -1 & -\frac{1}{2} & -\frac{1}{3} \\ 1 & 0 & -1 & -\frac{1}{2} \\ \frac{1}{2} & 1 & 0 & -1 \\ \frac{1}{3} & \frac{1}{2} & 1 & 0 \\ & & & & \ddots \end{pmatrix}$$

is bounded. ◀

Example 5.8. ▶ In the construction of almost all examples till now the spaces X and Y were the same. (The exceptions are among the square integrable kernels described in Lemma 4.1.) That fact makes the examples "stronger" in some sense, and perhaps prettier, but no more compelling; "mixed" examples are perfectly legitimate and can occur naturally.

In the simplest mixed case X consists of a single point of mass 1. A kernel in that case is naturally identified with a function k on Y. A necessary and sufficient condition that such a kernel be bounded is that the function k belong to $L^2(Y)$, and, in that case, the induced integral operator is naturally identified with the linear functional A on $L^2(Y)$ defined by

$$A g = \int k(y) g(y) \, dy.$$

The simplest non-trivial mixed kernels, which, however, are not usually studied as such, are given by sequences of measurable functions. If, indeed, $\{k_0, k_1, k_2, \ldots\}$

is a sequence of measurable functions on Y, it is natural to define a kernel k on $\mathbb{Z}_+ \times Y$ by

$$k(n, y) = \overline{k_n(y)}.$$

(It is sometimes convenient to use two-way sequences $\{k_n : n = 0, \pm 1, \pm 2, \ldots\}$ and, correspondingly, to use $\mathbb{Z}$ instead of $\mathbb{Z}_+$.)

A classical example of a mixed kernel is given by an orthonormal sequence of functions in $L^2(Y)$. Since $k(n, \cdot) = \overline{k_n}$, so that $k(n, \cdot) \in L^2(Y)$ for each n, it follows that if $g \in L^2(Y)$, then $k(n, \cdot) g \in L^1(Y)$ for each n. Since, moreover, $\int k(n, y) g(y) \, dy$ $(= \int g(y) \overline{k_n(y)} \, dy)$ is the n-th Fourier coefficient of g with respect to the orthonormal sequence k, it follows that the sequence $\{\int k(n, y) g(y) \, dy\}$ belongs to ℓ^2 $(= L^2(\mathbb{Z}_+))$, and its norm is dominated by $\|g\|$.

The analytically most important special case is the *discrete Fourier transform*. In that case $X = \mathbb{Z}$, $Y = \mathbb{I}$, and the kernel k is defined by

$$k(n, y) = e^{-2\pi i n y}, \qquad n = 0, \pm 1, \pm 2, \ldots .$$

Since $a(n) = (\text{Int } k) g(n)$ is the n-th Fourier coefficient of g, and since $\sum_n |a(n)|^2 = \|g\|^2$, it follows that the discrete Fourier transform is a unitary map (a surjective isometry) from $L^2(\mathbb{I})$ onto $L^2(\mathbb{Z})$. ◄

§6. Isomorphisms

Is there an integral operator on $L^2(\mathbb{II})$ that is a projection of infinite rank? For $\mathbb{R}_+$ the answer is yes (Example 5.1), but the construction seems to make use of the infinite amount of room in $\mathbb{R}_+$, i.e., of the infinite measure. The answer is yes for $\mathbb{II}$ also, and the proof is not difficult, but it is better understood and more useful if instead of being attacked head on, it is embedded into a larger context.

The point is that, in the study of integral operators, the measures μ and ν in the spaces X and Y are relatively unimportant; what matters much more is their measure class. In other words, what matters is the collection of measurable sets and the collection of sets of measure zero, or, better yet, what matters is the equivalence class of the measure (in the sense of absolute continuity).

The way to replace a measure by an equivalent one is to use a mapping appropriate to the category of measure spaces. Suppose, to be explicit, that X and X' are measure spaces, with measures μ and μ', and let φ be a mapping from X' to X that is measurable, absolutely continuous, and invertible. To say that φ is *measurable* means that $\varphi^{-1}(M)$ is a measurable subset of X' whenever M is a measurable subset of X. To say that φ is *absolutely continuous* means that $\mu'\varphi^{-1}(M)=0$ whenever $\mu(M)=0$, i.e., that the measure $\mu'\varphi^{-1}$ is absolutely continuous with respect to μ. To say, finally, that φ is *invertible* means that, except for sets of measure zero as usual, φ maps X' one-to-one onto X, and φ^{-1} has the same properties (measurable and absolutely continuous) as φ. It follows that the measures $\mu'\varphi^{-1}$ and μ are equivalent (in the sense of absolute continuity), and, consequently, that the Radon-Nikodym derivative $\delta=\dfrac{d\mu'\varphi^{-1}}{d\mu}$ is strictly positive almost everywhere.

Although mappings such as φ occur frequently in measure theory, they have no universally accepted name. Some authors have called them *isomorphisms* (occasionally with a modifier, such as "measure-theoretic"), and since that term seems inoffensive and adequately suggestive, it will be used in what follows.

Measure-theoretic isomorphisms such as φ induce mappings between function spaces: a function f on X becomes a function f' on X' by composition, $f'=f\circ\varphi$. These induced mappings are, however, too simple to be useful: there is, in general, no reason why an element f in $L^2(X)$ should get transformed into an element f' in $L^2(X')$. To pay for the way φ distorts measure, it is necessary to introduce a factor that restores the quantitative structure that put f into L^2 in the first place. The correct factor turns out to be $1/\sqrt{\delta\circ\varphi}$; the reason for the square root is the quadratic character of L^2.

Theorem 6.1. *If X and X' are (separable, σ-finite) measure spaces with measures μ and μ', if $\varphi: X' \to X$ is an isomorphism with $d\mu'\, \varphi^{-1}(x) = \delta(x)\, d\mu(x)$, and if for every (complex-valued) function f on X a function Uf is defined on X' by*

$$Uf(x') = \frac{1}{\sqrt{\delta(\varphi(x'))}}\, f(\varphi(x')),$$

then U maps $L^2(X)$ into $L^2(X')$, and, in fact, the restriction of U to $L^2(X)$ is a unitary map between the L^2 spaces (i.e., an isometric mapping from $L^2(X)$ onto $L^2(X')$).

▶ It is obvious that if f is measurable on X, then Uf is measurable on X' and that the mapping U is linear. Since, moreover,

$$\int \frac{|f(\varphi(x'))|^2}{\delta(\varphi(x'))}\, d\mu'(x') = \int \frac{|f(x)|^2}{\delta(x)}\, d\mu\, \varphi^{-1}(x) = \int |f(x)|^2\, d\mu(x),$$

it follows that the restriction of U to $L^2(X)$ is isometric.

The invertibility of φ implies that of U. Indeed, the inverse mapping

$$U^*: L^2(X') \to L^2(X)$$

is defined by

$$U^* f'(x) = \sqrt{\delta(x)}\, f'(\varphi^{-1}(x)).$$

To see that U^* maps $L^2(X')$ into $L^2(X)$, and isometrically at that, observe that

$$d\mu\, \varphi(x') = \frac{1}{\delta(\varphi(x'))}\, d\mu'(x'),$$

and apply the result of the preceding paragraph to X', X, U^*, and $1/\delta(\varphi(x'))$ in the place of X, X', U, and $\delta(x)$, respectively. To see that U^* is indeed the inverse of U, substitute:

$$U^* Uf(x) = \sqrt{\delta(x)}\, Uf(\varphi^{-1}(x)) = \sqrt{\delta(x)}\, \frac{1}{\sqrt{\delta(x)}}\, f(x).$$

The reverse computation, $U U^* f' = f'$, is in principle necessary, but, in view of the interchangeability of the roles of U and U^*, in the present case it follows from the direct one. ◀

Theorem 6.2. *Suppose that X, X', Y, Y' are (separable, σ-finite) measure spaces with measures μ, μ', ν, ν'. Suppose that*

$$\varphi: X' \to X \quad and \quad \psi: Y' \to Y$$

are isomorphisms, with

$$d\mu'\, \varphi^{-1}(x) = \delta(x)\, d\mu(x) \quad and \quad d\nu'\, \psi^{-1}(y) = \varepsilon(y)\, d\nu(y),$$

and let U and V be the induced unitary operators defined by

$$Uf(x') = \frac{1}{\sqrt{\delta(\varphi(x'))}} f(\varphi(x')) \quad \text{and} \quad Vg(y') = \frac{1}{\sqrt{\varepsilon(\psi(y'))}} g(\psi(y')).$$

For each function k on $X \times Y$, let Wk be the function k' on $X' \times Y'$ defined by

$$k'(x', y') = \frac{k(\varphi(x'), \psi(y'))}{\sqrt{\delta(\varphi(x')) \varepsilon(\psi(y'))}}.$$

If k is a bounded kernel, then so is k', and conversely; if Int $k = A$, then Int $k' = UAV^*$.

▶ Observe first that if k is measurable, then so is k'. Suppose now that k is a bounded kernel, and compute UAV^* as follows:

$$UAV^* g'(x') = \frac{1}{\sqrt{\delta(\varphi(x'))}} AV^* g'(\varphi(x'))$$

$$= \frac{1}{\sqrt{\delta(\varphi(x'))}} \int k(\varphi(x'), y) V^* g'(y) \, dv(y)$$

$$= \frac{1}{\sqrt{\delta(\varphi(x'))}} \int k(\varphi(x'), y) g'(\psi^{-1}(y)) \sqrt{\varepsilon(y)} \, dv(y)$$

$$= \frac{1}{\sqrt{\delta(\varphi(x'))}} \int k(\varphi(x'), y) \frac{1}{\sqrt{\varepsilon(y)}} g'(\psi^{-1}(y)) \varepsilon(y) \, dv(y)$$

$$= \int \frac{k(\varphi(x'), y)}{\sqrt{\delta(\varphi(x')) \varepsilon(y)}} g'(\psi^{-1}(y)) \, dv'(\psi^{-1}(y))$$

$$= \int \frac{k(\varphi(x'), \psi(y'))}{\sqrt{\delta(\varphi(x')) \varepsilon(\psi(y'))}} g'(y') \, dv'(y').$$

The computation implies that k' is a bounded kernel and that Int k' is exactly UAV^*.

The converse follows by an application of the direct result to the inverse of W. ◀

Corollary 6.3. *If $Y = X$, $Y' = X'$, and $\psi = \varphi$ (so that $V = U$), then Int $k' = UAU^*$ (so that Int k and Int k' are unitarily equivalent).* [10]

Corollary 6.4. *If k is a Carleman kernel, then so is k' and conversely; if k is square integrable, then so is k' and conversely, and, moreover, $\|k'\|_2 = \|k\|_2$.*

▶ If k is a Carleman kernel, then the unitary property of the induced operator V implies that $Vk(x, \cdot) \in L^2(Y')$ for almost every x. If x happens to be $\varphi(x')$, then

$$Vk(x, \cdot)(y') = \frac{1}{\sqrt{\varepsilon(\psi(y'))}} k(\varphi(x'), \psi(y'))$$

$$= \sqrt{\delta(\varphi(x'))} k'(x', y').$$

Since the factor $\sqrt{\delta(\varphi(x'))}$ is strictly positive almost everywhere, and since φ and ψ preserve the zeroness of measures, it follows that $k'(x', \cdot)$ is in $L^2(Y')$ for almost every x', i.e., that k' is a Carleman kernel. The converse follows by an application of the direct result to the inverse mappings.

If, finally, k is a square integrable kernel ($k \in L^2(X \times Y)$), then apply Theorem 6.1 to the W described in Theorem 6.2 to infer that the restriction of W to $L^2(X \times Y)$ is a unitary map onto $L^2(X' \times Y')$, and hence that $k'\ (= Wk)$ is square integrable also, with, moreover, the same Hilbert-Schmidt norm as k. The converse follows by an application of the direct result to the inverse of W. ◄

Example 6.5. ► The theorem yields more than existence; it yields explicit formulae. Consider, for instance, the measure spaces $X' = \mathbb{I}$ and $X = \mathbb{R}_+$, and let φ be the mapping from X' onto X defined by

$$\varphi(x') = \frac{x'}{1-x'}.$$

Since $\varphi^{-1}(x) = \dfrac{x}{1+x}$, it follows that the Radon-Nikodym derivative $\delta\left(= \dfrac{d\mu'\,\varphi^{-1}}{d\mu} \right)$ is given by

$$\delta(x) = \frac{1}{(1+x)^2},$$

so that

$$\sqrt{\delta(\varphi(x'))} = 1-x'.$$

The induced isometry U from $L^2(\mathbb{R}_+)$ onto $L^2(\mathbb{I})$ is defined by

$$Uf(x') = \frac{1}{1-x'}\, f\left(\frac{x'}{1-x'} \right);$$

correspondingly, a kernel k on $\mathbb{R}_+ \times \mathbb{R}_+$ becomes a kernel $k' = Wk$ on $\mathbb{I} \times \mathbb{I}$ given by

$$k'(x', y') = \frac{k\left(\dfrac{x'}{1-x'}, \dfrac{y'}{1-y'} \right)}{(1-x')(1-y')}.$$

The kernel k of the projection described in Example 5.1 can be pictured as follows:

An application of the mapping used above $\left(\varphi(x')=\dfrac{x'}{1-x'}\right)$ converts this into a kernel on the unit square given by

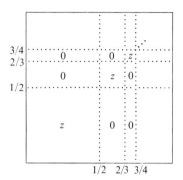

where z denotes $\dfrac{1}{(1-x)(1-y)}$. Consequence: there is an integral operator on $L^2(\mathbb{I})$ that is a projection of infinite rank. To get an orthonormal basis for the range of Int k, normalize the functions that are $\dfrac{1}{1-x}$ in $\left(\dfrac{n}{n+1},\dfrac{n+1}{n+2}\right)$ and 0 elsewhere, $n=0,1,2,\dots$. ◄

Example 6.6 ► Consider an atomic measure space X, with measure μ, and assume, with no loss of measure-theoretic generality, that $\mu(\{x\})>0$ for each x in X. If X' is the set X with the counting measure μ', then there is a natural map $\varphi\colon X'\to X$, namely the identity map. It is easy to compute δ and U in this case. Since

$$1=\mu'(\{x\})=\mu'\varphi^{-1}(\{x\})=\delta(x)\mu(\{x\}),$$

it follows that

$$\delta(x)=\frac{1}{\mu(\{x\})},$$

and hence that

$$Uf(x)=\frac{1}{\sqrt{\mu(\{x\})}}f(x).$$

Consequence (in view of Theorem 6.2): the only atomic spaces that need ever to be considered in the theory of integral operators are the ones with the counting measure. ◄

The moral of Theorem 6.2 and Examples 6.5 and 6.6 is that indeed the structure of integral operators does not depend on the underlying *measure* but on its *measure class* only. Thus, for instance, it does not matter at all whether the underlying measures are finite or not; the existence or non-existence of atoms is much more important. For constructing counterexamples, therefore, infinite measures are just as good as finite ones; if something can go wrong in the infinite case, it can go wrong in the finite case too. For proving theorems, on the other hand, finite measures are just as good as infinite ones; if something is well-behaved in the finite case, it will be well-behaved in the infinite case too.

§7. Algebra

Bounded kernels induce bounded operators; what is the relation between the various ways of constructing new kernels out of old (such as sum, convolution, transpose) and the various ways of constructing new operators out of old (such as sum, product, adjoint)? The answers are sometimes easy, sometimes not so easy, and sometimes unknown.

There is nothing interesting to be said about addition: it works smoothly. That is: if h and k are bounded kernels and $h+k$ is their pointwise sum, then $h+k$ is bounded and

$$\text{Int} (h+k) = \text{Int } h + \text{Int } k.$$

The same is true of multiplication by a scalar. That is: if k is a bounded kernel, if α is a scalar, and if a kernel αk is defined by $(\alpha k)(x, y) = \alpha \cdot k(x, y)$, then αk is a bounded kernel and

$$\text{Int} (\alpha k) = \alpha \cdot \text{Int } k.$$

In other words: the set of all bounded kernels on $X \times Y$ is a vector space, and the restriction of Int to that vector space is a linear transformation into the set of all bounded operators from $L^2(Y)$ to $L^2(X)$. The proof is an obvious verification.

There is nothing interesting to be said about convolution either: no general theorem seems to be known about it. It seems right to call two kernels h and k, on $X \times Y$ and $Y \times Z$ respectively, *multipliable* ("convolutable" might be better, but it doesn't sound right) if

$$h(x, \cdot) k(\cdot, z) \in L^1(Y)$$

for almost every $\langle x, z \rangle$. In that case the convolution

$$\int h(x, y) k(y, z) \, dy$$

can be formed for almost every $\langle x, z \rangle$; it defines a kernel on $X \times Z$.

Problem 7.1. ▶ Are two bounded kernels always multipliable? The answer turns out to be no. For an example, suppose that X, Y, and Z are measure spaces, k is a bounded kernel on $Y \times Z$, and u and v are elements of $L^2(X)$ and $L^2(Y)$ respectively such that $u \neq 0$ and $\int |k(y, z) v(y)| \, dy = \infty$ on a set of positive measure in Z. If h is defined by $h(x, y) = u(x) \overline{v(y)}$, then h is a Hilbert-Schmidt kernel, and h and k are not multipliable. Examples of such k's, u's, and v's are easy to come by. They do not, however, answer all sensible questions. Thus, for instance, *is the convolution of two multipliable bounded kernels necessarily bounded? If a convolution is bounded, does it necessarily induce the product operator?* ◄

Comment: for matrices the answers are classical and easy; all the answers are yes. Indeed, if a is a matrix and $A = \text{Int } a$, so that

$$A g(i) = \sum_j a(i, j) g(j),$$

and if e_p is, for each p, the characteristic function of $\{p\}$, then

$$(A e_j, e_i) = \sum_p \sum_q a(p, q) e_j(q) e_i(p) = a(i, j).$$

It follows that if a and b are matrices, with $A = \text{Int } a$ and $B = \text{Int } b$, then the matrix c of AB is given by

$$c(i, j) = (AB e_j, e_i) = (B e_j, A^* e_i)$$
$$= (\sum_p (B e_j, e_p) e_p, A^* e_i)$$
$$= \sum_p (B e_j, e_p)(e_p, A^* e_i)$$
$$= \sum_p (A e_p, e_i)(B e_j, e_p) = \sum_p a(i, p) b(p, j).$$

One of the subtlest parts of the theory of kernels concerns their relation to adjoints. Recall that if A is a bounded linear transformation from $L^2(Y)$ into $L^2(X)$, then the adjoint A^* makes sense; it is the bounded linear transformation from $L^2(X)$ into $L^2(Y)$ uniquely determined by the requirement that

$$(A^* f, g) = (f, A g)$$

whenever $f \in L^2(X)$ and $g \in L^2(Y)$. If k is a bounded kernel on $X \times Y$, does it follow that the conjugate transpose k^* is a bounded kernel on $Y \times X$ and $A^* = \text{Int } k^*$? No, it does not.

Example 7.2. Let A be the discrete Fourier transform (Example 5.8), i.e., the integral operator induced by the kernel k defined on $\mathbb{Z} \times \mathbb{I}$ by $k(n, y) = e^{-2\pi i n y}$ $(= \overline{e_n(y)})$. The transformation $\text{Int } k$ assigns to each g in $L^2(\mathbb{I})$ the sequence of its Fourier coefficients; the adjoint A^* assigns to each sequence f in $L^2(\mathbb{Z})$ the function whose sequence of Fourier coefficients it is. (Formal check:

$$(\sum_n f(n) e_n, g) = \sum_n f(n) \overline{(g, e_n)} = (f, A g).)$$

The transformation A^* deserves to be called the *compact Fourier transform.*[11] Is it true that $A^* = \text{Int } k^*$? No, it's as false as it can be: k^* is not a bounded kernel, and A^* is not an integral operator.

▶ The proof has two steps: (1) if there were a kernel h on $\mathbb{I} \times \mathbb{Z}$ such that $A^* = \text{Int } h$, then h would have to be defined by $h(y, n) = e^{2\pi i n y} (= k^*(y, n))$, and (2) the kernel k^* is not bounded.

Indeed: if $\sum_n h(y, n) f(n) = (\sum f(n) e_n)(y)$ whenever $f \in L^2(\mathbb{Z})$, then choose f to be the characteristic function of a singleton $\{n\}$ and conclude that $h(y, n) = e_n(y) = k^*(y, n)$. If k^* were bounded, then it would follow that $k^*(y, \cdot) f$ would belong to $L^1(\mathbb{Z})$ whenever $f \in L^2(\mathbb{Z})$. That is, it would follow that $\sum_n |f(n)| < \infty$ whenever $\sum_n |f(n)|^2 < \infty$, and that is absurd. (Remember the harmonic series.)

It might seem that the reason for the success of this example is that the measure of $\mathbb{Z}$ is infinite. Can a similar counterexample be made using finite measures only? The answer is yes: just use Theorem 6.2, with an isomorphism φ that maps $\mathbb{Z}$ onto an atomic space of finite measure (and with the identity mapping in the role of ψ).

Is it the atomic character of $\mathbb{Z}$ that makes for pathology? Can a similar counterexample be made using divisible measures only? The answer is yes again; what is needed is the tensor product (inflation) technique mentioned in §2 and used in §6. Explicitly: define k on $\mathbb{R} \times \mathbb{I}$ by

$$k(x, y) = e^{-2\pi i [x] y};$$

here $[x]$ is the greatest integer below x. (The kernel k is the tensor product of the kernel of the discrete Fourier transform and the kernel k' on $\mathbb{I} \times \mathbb{Z}_1$ defined by $k'(x, 1) = 1$.) The verification that k is bounded is straightforward: if $g \in L^2(\mathbb{I})$, then

$$\int |\int k(x, y) g(y) \, dy|^2 \, dx = \sum_n \int_n^{n+1} |\int k(x, y) g(y) \, dy|^2 \, dx$$

$$= \sum_n \left| \int_0^1 e^{-2\pi i n y} g(y) \, dy \right|^2 = \sum_n |(g, e_n)|^2 = \|g\|^2.$$

The operator $A = \text{Int } k$ assigns to each g in $L^2(\mathbb{I})$ the function on $\mathbb{R}$ whose value between n and $n+1$ is the constant equal to the Fourier coefficient (g, e_n); the adjoint A^* assigns to each function f in $L^2(\mathbb{R})$ the functions whose n-th Fourier coefficient is the average $\int_n^{n+1} f(x) \, dx$ of f between n and $n+1$. (Formal check:

$$\left(\sum_n \left(\int_n^{n+1} f(x) \, dx \right) e_n, g \right) = \sum_n \left(\int_n^{n+1} f(x) \, dx \right) \overline{(g, e_n)}$$

$$= \int f(x) \overline{(\int k(x, y) g(y) \, dy)} \, dx = (f, A g).)$$

The inflated compact Fourier transform has the same bad properties as the uninflated one, and the proof is essentially the same.

(1) If $A^* = \text{Int } h$, then $\left(\sum_n \left(\int_n^{n+1} f(x) \, dx \right) e_n \right)(y) = \int h(y, x) f(x) \, dx$ almost every-where for each f in $L^2(\mathbb{R})$. If f vanishes outside $(n, n+1)$, then

$$\left(\int_n^{n+1} f(x) \, dx \right) e_n(y) = \int_n^{n+1} h(y, x) f(x) \, dx,$$

so that the transform of each such f is a constant multiple of e_n. By Lemma 4.3, $h(y, x) = u(y)\overline{v(x)}$ almost everywhere on $(n, n+1) \times \mathbb{I}$. It follows (set $f = 1$ on $(n, n+1)$) that $u(y) = e^{2\pi i n y}$; since, moreover,

$$\int_n^{n+1} f(x)\, dx = \int_n^{n+1} \overline{v(x)} f(x)\, dx$$

no matter what f is, it follows that $v(x) = 1$ on $(n, n+1)$. Consequence: $h(y, x) = e^{2\pi i [x] y} = k^*(y, x) (= \overline{k(x, y)})$.

(2) The proof that k^* is not bounded is easier, and even more like the uninflated case. If k^* were bounded, then f in $L^2(\mathbb{R})$ would imply $k^*(y, \cdot) f$ in $L^1(\mathbb{R})$, i.e.,

$$\int_{-\infty}^{+\infty} |f(x)|^2\, dx < \infty \quad \text{would imply} \quad \int_{-\infty}^{+\infty} |f(x)|\, dx < \infty, \text{ which is absurd.}$$

With one alteration the compact Fourier transform was transplanted to a finite measure space and with another one to a divisible measure space. Can it be transplanted to a measure space that is both finite and divisible? Yes – trivially: use inflation to make the space divisible (as above), and then use isomorphism (Theorem 6.2) to make it finite. ◀

One of the best ways to study a concept is to get a feeling for its boundaries by looking at examples and counterexamples. As far as integral operators are concerned, there are several examples in §5, but, for all that was said before Example 7.2, the concept had no boundaries: it was conceivable that every operator from $L^2(Y)$ into $L^2(X)$ is an integral operator. The example of the compact Fourier transform rules out that possibility, but the reason why it works still deserves some study. Just what is the big difference between the discrete Fourier transform and the compact one? Here is at least a part of the answer.

Theorem 7.3. *If X is atomic, then every bounded linear transformation from $L^2(Y)$ into $L^2(X)$ is an integral operator.*

▶ In view of the isomorphism theorem (cf. also Example 6.6), it is sufficient to treat the case $X = \mathbb{Z}_+$. In that case, let e_n be the characteristic function of the singleton $\{n\}$. If A is a bounded linear transformation from $L^2(Y)$ to $L^2(X)$ $(= \ell^2)$, define a kernel k by

$$k(n, y) = \overline{A^* e_n(y)}.$$

It follows that if $g \in L^2(Y)$, then

$$A g(n) = (A g, e_n) = (g, A^* e_n) = \int k(n, y) g(y)\, dy. \quad ◀$$

Theorem 7.3 includes, of course, the representability of operators by matrices. If, for instance, $X = Y = \mathbb{Z}_+$, then a kernel on $X \times Y$ is an infinite matrix, and every operator A from $L^2(Y)$ into $L^2(X)$ can be defined by an equation of the form

$$A g(i) = \sum_j a(i, j) g(j).$$

Theorem 7.3 indicates that the answer to the question "which operators are integral?" depends on the underlying spaces. If X is atomic, all is well; if, however, all that is assumed is that Y is atomic, then the compact Fourier transform shows that there can be trouble. (Small notational collision with Example 7.2: there X was $\mathbb{Z}$ and Y was $\mathbb{I}$, but, to see the trouble, here the roles of $\mathbb{Z}$ and $\mathbb{I}$ should be interchanged.)

The bad news about adjoints (Example 7.2) is that the conjugate transpose of a bounded kernel may fail to be bounded and the adjoint of an integral operator may fail to be an integral operator. The good news is that the two things that can go wrong necessarily happen together. A convenient proof depends on the following auxiliary statement.

Lemma 7.4 *If k is a bounded kernel on $X \times Y$, then $X \times Y$ is the union of an increasing sequence of measurable rectangles of finite measure on each of which k is integrable.*

The statement goes in the opposite direction to that of Theorem B1. There the assertion is that kernels may fail to be approximable by their pointwise bounded restrictions to measurable rectangles. The present result offers a good substitute; it says that bounded kernels (in the operator sense) are approximable by their analytically "small" restrictions to measurable rectangles.

▶ Since X and Y are σ-finite, there exist increasing sequences $\{X_1, X_2, ...\}$ and $\{Y_1, Y_2, ...\}$ of sets of finite measure such that $X_n \uparrow X$ and $Y_n \uparrow Y$. Since the characteristic function of Y_n belongs to $L^2(Y)$, it follows that $k(x, \cdot)$ times that function belongs to $L^1(Y)$ for almost every x, i.e., that

$$\int_{Y_n} |k(x, y)| \, dy < \infty$$

almost everywhere. It is convenient and harmless to assume that the integrals are, in fact, finite everywhere. The idea of the rest of the proof is to approximate X by a sequence of sets on which $\int_{Y_n} |k(x, y)| \, dy$ is bounded. Since that sequence depends on n, so that there is really a sequence of sequences, an additional piece of arithmetic is needed to get the desired conclusion. The details go as follows.

Whenever m and n are positive integers, write

$$X_{nm} = X_m \cap \{x: \int_{Y_n} |k(x, y)| \, dy \le m\}.$$

For each temporarily fixed n, the sequence $\{X_{n1}, X_{n2}, ...\}$ is an increasing sequence of sets of finite measure such that $X_{nm} \uparrow X$. The conclusion of the lemma is satisfied by the measurable rectangles $\left(\bigcup_{i=1}^{n} X_{in}\right) \times Y_n$, $n = 1, 2, 3, ...$. Indeed: if $\langle x, y \rangle \in X \times Y$, find n_0 so that $y \in Y_{n_0}$, and then find m_0 so that $x \in X_{n_0, m_0}$. If $n \ge n_0$ and $n \ge m_0$, then $x \in X_{n_0, m_0} \subset X_{n_0, n} \subset \bigcup_{i=1}^{n} X_{in}$ and $y \in Y_{n_0} \subset Y_n$. This proves that the sequence $\{X_n \times Y_n\}$

$\left(\text{where, of course, } X_n = \bigcup_{i=1}^{n} X_{in}\right)$ is increasing and has $X \times Y$ for its union. Since $\int_{Y_n} |k(x, y)| \, dy \leq n$ when $x \in X_n$, Fubini's theorem implies that k is integrable on each $X_n \times Y_n$, and the proof of the lemma is complete. ◄

Theorem 7.5. *The conjugate transpose of a bounded kernel is bounded if and only if the adjoint of the induced integral operator is an integral operator, and, in that case,* Int $k^* = (\text{Int } k)^*$.[12]

▶ Assume, to begin with, that k is a kernel such that both k and k^* are bounded. It is to be proved that if $A = \text{Int } k$ and $B = \text{Int } k^*$, then $B = A^*$. The idea is to show that the sesquilinear forms of B and of A^* agree on functions that are not too large, and then to argue by approximation.

Apply Lemma 7.4 to get a sequence $\{X_n \times Y_n\}$ of measurable rectangles of finite measure on each of which k is integrable. Let f on X and g on Y be bounded measurable functions that vanish outside X_n and Y_n respectively, for some n; note that the set of such f's is dense in $L^2(X)$, and, similarly, the set of such g's is dense in $L^2(Y)$. The integrability of k on $X_n \times Y_n$ implies that the function p defined by

$$p(x, y) = f(x) k(x, y) g(y)$$

is in $L^1(X \times Y)$, and that therefore

$$(A^*f, g) = (f, A g) = \int f(x) \overline{\left(\int k(x, y) g(y) \, dy\right)} \, dx$$
$$= \int \left(\int f(x) k^*(y, x) \, dx\right) \overline{g(y)} \, dy = (Bf, g).$$

The extreme terms of this chain of equations depend continuously on f and g; it follows that the sesquilinear forms are indeed identical.

Suppose next that k is a bounded kernel on $X \times Y$ such that if $A = \text{Int } k$, then $A^* = \text{Int } h$ for some bounded kernel h on $Y \times X$. It is to be proved that $h = k^*$. The idea is to show that h and k^* agree on certain large sets and then argue by exhaustion.

Apply Lemma 7.4 separately to the kernels h and k and then form the sequence of intersections of the two sequences so obtained. The result is a sequence $\{X_n \times Y_n\}$ of measurable rectangles of finite measure on each of which both h and k are integrable. (The preceding sentences contain a minor notational solecism. The kernel k is defined on $X \times Y$ and the kernel h on $Y \times X$. For the two sequences of measurable rectangles to be comparable, one of them has to be turned around in an obvious sense.) Consider now functions f and g, exactly as in the first part of the proof, so that both the functions p and q, defined by

$$p(x, y) = f(x) h(y, x) g(y)$$

and

$$q(x, y) = f(x) k(x, y) g(y)$$

are in $L^1(X \times Y)$. It follows that

$$\int(\int f(x)\,h(y,x)\,dx)\,\overline{g(y)}\,dy = (A^*f,g) = (f,Ag)$$
$$= \int f(x)(\overline{\int k(x,y)\,g(y)\,dy})\,dx$$
$$= \int(\int f(x)\,\overline{k(x,y)}\,dx)\,\overline{g(y)}\,dy.$$

The equality of the extreme terms of this chain for all the g's under consideration implies that, for each f,

$$\int f(x)\,h(y,x)\,dx = \int f(x)\,\overline{k(x,y)}\,dx$$

almost everywhere in Y. The validity of this equality for all the f's under consideration implies in turn that

$$h(y,x) = \overline{k(x,y)} = k^*(y,x)$$

almost everywhere in $X \times Y$. (The cautious way to phrase the last argument is to restrict attention to a countable dense subset of the f's.) ◄

Corollary 7.6. *If k is a bounded kernel on $X \times Y$ and if Y is atomic, then k^* is a bounded kernel on $X \times Y$ and* $\operatorname{Int} k^* = (\operatorname{Int} k)^*$.

▶ By Theorem 7.3 (with the roles of X and Y interchanged) the adjoint $(\operatorname{Int} k)^*$ is an integral operator from $L^2(X)$ to $L^2(Y)$, and therefore, by Theorem 7.5, k^* is a bounded kernel on $Y \times X$. ◄

Corollary 7.7. *If k is a bounded matrix, then so is k^*, and* $\operatorname{Int} k^* = (\operatorname{Int} k)^*$.

§8. Uniqueness

The restriction of Int to the vector space of all bounded kernels on $X \times Y$ is a linear transformation into the set of all bounded operators from $L^2(Y)$ to $L^2(X)$. It is natural to ask: is that linear transformation injective? In other words: is an integral operator induced by only one kernel? The content of the following assertion is that the answer is yes.

Theorem 8.1. *If a bounded kernel k induces the integral operator 0, then $k(x, y)=0$ for almost every $\langle x, y \rangle$.*[13]

▶ If Y_0 is a measurable subset of Y, then the restriction of k to $X \times Y_0$ is a bounded kernel; it is therefore sufficient to prove the theorem under the added assumption that the measure of Y is finite. (The standing assumptions of separability and σ-finiteness are in force.) Under that assumption $1 \in L^2(Y)$, and therefore $k(x, \cdot) \cdot 1 \in L^1(Y)$ for almost every x; it is only a change of notation to assume that $k(x, \cdot) \in L^1(Y)$ for *every* x.

Since $L^1(Y)$ is separable, and since a subset of a separable metric space is separable, there exists a countable collection of measurable sets (of finite measure) in Y such that their characteristic functions $\{\chi_1, \chi_2, ...\}$ form a set dense in the set of all characteristic functions in $L^1(Y)$. Let E_0 be a set of measure zero (in X) such that if $x \notin E_0$ then $\int k(x, y) \chi_n(y) \, dy = 0$; such an E_0 exists because, by assumption, k induces the integral operator 0.

Consider now an arbitrary measurable set (of finite measure) in Y, with characteristic function χ. Find an increasing sequence $\{n_1, n_2, ...\}$ of positive integers so that $\chi_{n_j} \to \chi$ almost everywhere. (A subsequence of a sequence for which $\chi_{n_j} \to \chi$ in $L^1(Y)$ will do.) For each x, the sequence $\{k(x, \cdot) \chi_{n_j}\}$ converges almost everywhere to $k(x, \cdot) \chi$; since $\{k(x, \cdot) \chi_{n_j}\}$ converges dominatedly (in $L^1(Y)$) to $k(x, \cdot) \chi$ almost everywhere, it follows that if $x \notin E_0$, then $\int k(x, y) \chi(y) \, dy = 0$. Equivalently, the function $k(x, \cdot)$ has the property that its indefinite integral is 0, and hence that $k(x, y)=0$ for almost every y (whenever $x \notin E_0$). Since k is a measurable function on $X \times Y$, the proof of the uniqueness theorem is complete. ◀

Problem 8.2. ▶ According to Theorem 8.1 a kernel k is uniquely determined by the induced integral operator Int k. *Can the determination be made explicit? Is there, that is, an "effective procedure" for recapturing the kernel from the operator?* ◀

Comment: for matrices (where both X and Y are atomic) the answer is classical and easy, and that answer is easily generalizable to the case where only one of X and Y is assumed to be atomic. Indeed, if $X = \mathbb{Z}$ and

$$A g(n) = \int k(n, y) g(y) \, dy,$$

then the relations

$$A g(n) = (A g, e_n) = (g, A^* e_n)$$

(where e_n is the characteristic function of $\{n\}$), and

$$\int k(n, y) g(y) \, dy = (g, \overline{k(n, \cdot)}),$$

show that

$$k(n, \cdot) = \overline{A^* e_n};$$

cf. the proof of Theorem 7.3. If, on the other hand, $Y = \mathbb{Z}$, and

$$A g(x) = \sum_p k(x, p) g(p),$$

then, in particular,

$$k(x, n) = \sum_p k(x, p) e_n(p) = A e_n(x).$$

Why is a kernel always defined as a *measurable* function on $X \times Y$? The answer seems to be that an analyst finds it hard to pronounce the word "function" without at least thinking "measurable". For a kernel k to be analytically usable, one-variable functions such as $k(x, \cdot)$ and $\int k(\cdot, y) g(y) \, dy$ must be measurable. If k itself is measurable, then the measurability of those functions follows, but the measurability of the two-variable function is almost never used; the proof of Theorem 8.1 is a rare exception.

Example 8.3. ▶ Write $X = Y = \mathbb{I}$, and let M be a subset of $X \times Y$ such that each vertical section M_x is countable and the complement $X - M^y$ of each horizontal section is countable. If k is the characteristic function of M, then, for each x, $k(x, y) = 0$ for almost every y, and, therefore, k induces the linear transformation 0. What this example shows is that even a non-measurable kernel can yield an operator. The operator it yields is, to be sure, induced by a measurable kernel also (namely $k(x, y) \equiv 0$). ◀ [14]

Problem 8.4. ▶ *If a non-measurable kernel induces an operator from $L^2(Y)$ into $L^2(X)$, is there always a measurable kernel that induces the same operator?* The problem is probably not an important one for the theory of integral operators, but it does seem to be unsolved. In precise terms the problem can be stated as follows. Suppose that k is a function on $X \times Y$ such that (1) for almost every x, $k(x, \cdot)$ is measurable and $k(x, \cdot) g \in L^1(Y)$ whenever $g \in L^2(Y)$, and (2) if $g \in L^2(Y)$ and $f(x) = \int k(x, y) g(y) \, dy$, then f (is measurable and) belongs to $L^2(Y)$; does it then follow that there exists a measurable function k' on $X \times Y$ such that, for almost every x, $k(x, y) = k'(x, y)$ for almost every y? ◄

Theorem 8.1, the uniqueness theorem, says that the restriction of Int to bounded kernels on $X \times Y$ is injective. Whether that restriction is surjective or not depends on the underlying spaces: if X is atomic, then the answer is yes (Theorem 7.3), but sometimes the answer is no (Example 7.2). The negative answer is not rare, and, as the following theorem shows, examples to establish it do not have to be pathological in any sense of the word.

Theorem 8.5. *The identity operator on $L^2(\mathbb{I})$ is not an integral operator.*[15]

▶ Suppose that k is a bounded kernel on $\mathbb{I} \times \mathbb{I}$, fix a number t, $0 < t < 1$, and consider the restriction k_t of k to $(0, t) \times (t, 1)$.
If $g \in L^2(\mathbb{I})$, then

$$\int_t^1 k_t(x, y) g(y) \, dy = \int_t^1 k(x, y) g(y) \, dy;$$

if, moreover, $g \in L^2(t, 1)$, then

$$\int_t^1 k(x, y) g(y) \, dy = \int_0^1 k(x, y) g(y) \, dy;$$

and if, finally, k induces the identity operator on $L^2(\mathbb{I})$, then

$$\int_0^1 k(x, y) g(y) \, dy = g(x) = 0$$

for almost every x. Consequence (by the uniqueness theorem): $k_t(x, y) = 0$ almost everywhere, or, equivalently, $k(x, y) = 0$ almost everywhere in $(0, t) \times (t, 1)$. Similar reasoning (restrict k to $(t, 1) \times (0, t)$ and apply to $L^2(0, t)$) implies that $k(x, y) = 0$ almost everywhere in $(t, 1) \times (0, t)$. Since countably many rectangles such as $(0, t) \times (t, 1)$ and $(t, 1) \times (0, t)$ cover almost all of $\mathbb{I} \times \mathbb{I}$, it follows that $k = 0$ almost everywhere. ◄

The use of a little more analytic machinery can produce a powerful analytic strengthening of Theorem 8.5.

Theorem 8.6. *If $\varphi \in L^\infty(\mathbb{I})$, if A is the multiplication operator induced by φ (i.e., $Af(x) = \varphi(x) f(x)$ almost everywhere whenever $f \in L^2(\mathbb{I})$), and if k is a bounded kernel on $\mathbb{I} \times \mathbb{I}$, then*

$$\|A - \operatorname{Int} k\| \geq \|\varphi\|_2.$$

Remark: the statement is restricted to $L^2(\mathbb{I})$, but that is for convenience only. With minor adaptations the proof works for divisible spaces in general, whether the measure be finite or infinite, or alternatively, a proof for divisible spaces can be based on the result for II.

▶ Let $\{e_n\}$ be the usual exponential basis for $L^2(\text{II})$ $(e_n(x)=e^{2\pi inx},\ n=0,\pm1,$ $\pm2,\dots)$. Since $e_0\in L^2$, therefore $k(x,\cdot)\in L^1$ for almost every x. For the "good" x's (i.e., the ones not belonging to the exceptional set of measure zero) the Riemann-Lebesgue lemma implies that the integrals

$$\int k(x,y)\,e_n(y)\,dy$$

tend to 0 as $n\to\infty$.[16] Since $|e_n(x)|=1$ always, it follows that if $f_n=(A-\text{Int }k)\,e_n$, then $|f_n(x)|\to|\varphi(x)|$ for almost every x. Apply Fatou's lemma to the sequence $\{|f_n|^2\}$. The result is that

$$\|\varphi\|_2^2=\int|\varphi(x)|^2\,dx=\int\lim_n|f_n(x)|^2\,dx$$

$$\leq\liminf_n\int|f_n(x)|^2\,dx=\liminf_n\|f_n\|^2$$

$$=\liminf_n\|(A-\text{Int }k)\,e_n\|^2\leq\|A-\text{Int }k\|^2.\ \blacktriangleleft^{17}$$

§9. Tensors

The tensor product of two Hilbert spaces is sometimes called their "direct product". The direct sum of two Hilbert spaces is never called their "tensor sum", but it might as well be; its formation is in some respects like that of the tensor product, and direct sums and tensor products of copies of a Hilbert space are used to form the "tensor algebra" of that space. The purpose of this section is to study the related theory of direct sums and tensor products of kernels and their relation to boundedness.[18]

Direct sums are easy enough.

Theorem 9.1. *The direct sum* $\sum_j \oplus k_j$ *of a bounded countable set of bounded kernels is a bounded kernel; the integral operator it induces is the direct sum* $\sum_j \oplus \operatorname{Int} k_j$ *of the integral operators that the summands separately induce.*

▶ The assumption is that each kernel k_j is bounded and that the set of numbers $\|k_j\|$ is bounded. The statement is clear and probably intuitively obvious; in any event, once either the underlying geometry or the notational algebra is clearly described the proof becomes trivial.

Suppose, to be explicit, that k_j is defined on $X_j \times Y_j$, where the spaces X_j are pairwise disjoint and the spaces Y_j are pairwise disjoint; write $X = \bigcup_j X_j$ and $Y = \bigcup_j Y_j$. If $g \in L^2(Y)$, write g_j for the projection of g into $L^2(Y_j)$, i.e., $g_j(y) = g(y)$ when $y \in Y_j$ and $g_j(y) = 0$ otherwise. If $x \in X_j$, then $k(x, y) g(y) = k_j(x, y) g_j(y)$ when $y \in Y_j$ and 0 otherwise. Since the boundedness of k_j implies that

$$k_j(x, \cdot) g_j \in L^1(X_j) \qquad \text{for almost every } x \text{ in } X_j,$$

it follows that

$$k(x, \cdot) g \in L^1(X) \qquad \text{for almost every } x \text{ in } X.$$

If $f(x) = \int k(x, y) g(y) \, dy$ and if $x \in X_j$, then

$$f(x) = \int k_j(x, y) g_j(y) \, dy$$

(except, as always, for a set of x's of measure zero). Since

$$(\operatorname{Int} k_j) g_j \in L^2(X_j) \quad \text{and} \quad \|(\operatorname{Int} k_j) g_j\| \leq \|k_j\| \cdot \|g_j\|,$$

and since $f=\sum_j(\operatorname{Int}k_j)g_j$ (where the series converges in L^2 and also almost everywhere), it follows that

$$\int|f(x)|^2\,dx=\int|\sum_j(\operatorname{Int}k_j)\,g_j(y)|^2\,dy$$
$$=\int\sum_j|(\operatorname{Int}k_j)\,g_j(y)|^2\,dy.$$

(Note: distinct $(\operatorname{Int}k_j)\,g_j$'s have disjoint supports.) Hence

$$\int|f(x)|^2\,dx=\sum_j\int|(\operatorname{Int}k_j)\,g_j(y)|^2\,dy$$
$$=\sum_j\|(\operatorname{Int}k_j)\,g_j\|^2\leq\sum_j\|k_j\|^2\cdot\|g_j\|^2$$
$$\leq\sup_j\|k_j\|^2\cdot\sum_j\|g_j\|^2=\sup_j\|k_j\|^2\cdot\|g\|^2.\quad\blacktriangleleft$$

Corollary 9.2. *The direct sum of a bounded countable set of bounded Carleman kernels is a bounded Carleman kernel.*

Note: the assertion of the corollary for Hilbert-Schmidt in place of Carleman is false. Example: the infinite identity matrix.

Treatments of direct sums (of Hilbert spaces and of operators) can be found in many places, probably because they are not needed; the theory is so easy as to be practically automatic. Treatments of tensor products are much less easy to find, and the theory is slightly harder.

As far as the underlying Hilbert spaces go, in the context of integral operators only L^2 spaces need to be considered, and for them a brisk definition of tensor product is available: the *tensor product* $L^2(X)\otimes L^2(X')$ can be defined as $L^2(X\times X')$. If f and f' are elements of $L^2(X)$ and $L^2(X')$ respectively, their tensor product $f\otimes f'$ (cf. Example 4.2) is a particular element of $L^2(X)\otimes L^2(X')$.

The restriction of Int to $L^2(X\times X')$ is a natural one-to-one correspondence between $L^2(X\times X')$ and the set of Hilbert-Schmidt operators from $L^2(X')$ to $L^2(X)$ (cf. Lemma 4.1). In view of this correspondence, the tensor product of $L^2(X)$ and $L^2(X')$ might as well be defined as that set of Hilbert-Schmidt operators. That definition extends to arbitrary Hilbert spaces (not necessarily represented as L^2 spaces). If u and u' are elements of H and H' respectively, then their tensor product $u\otimes u'$, as a Hilbert-Schmidt operator (of rank 1) from H' to H is defined by

(1) $\qquad (u\otimes u')f'=(f',u')u.$

Note that if H and H' are $L^2(X)$ and $L^2(X')$, then the two possible interpretations of $u\otimes u'$ are in harmony; the function $u\otimes u'$ on $X\times X'$, regarded as a kernel, induces the integral operator $u\otimes u'$ from $L^2(X')$ to $L^2(X)$. In what follows, the first definition ($L^2(X\times X')$) of tensor product will be regarded as the official one, but its equivalence with the second definition (Hilbert-Schmidt) will be used as a convenient tool.

The useful aspect of tensor products concerns not spaces but operators. If A: $K \to H$ and A': $K' \to H'$ are operators, the problem is to construct a tensor product $A \otimes A'$: $K \otimes K' \to H \otimes H'$ so that if $g \in K$ and $g' \in K'$ then $(A \otimes A')(g \otimes g') = Ag \otimes A'g'$. Attempts to meet the problem head-on are not likely to be successful; there are some boundedness subtleties. Many of them evaporate, however, or, more fairly said, are absorbed by an already developed theory, if Hilbert-Schmidt operators are used.

To get a clue to the right way to define $A \otimes A'$, consider the relation between the Hilbert-Schmidt operators T: $K' \to K$ and S: $H' \to H$ defined via elements v in K and v' in K' by

$$T = v \otimes v', \quad S = Av \otimes A'v'.$$

If $f' \in H'$, then

$$Sf' = (f', A'v') Av = A[((A')^* f', v') v]$$
$$= AT(A')^* f',$$

so that

(2) $\qquad S = AT(A')^*.$

That is the clue.

Theorem 9.3. *If A and A' are bounded linear transformations from $L^2(Y)$ to $L^2(X)$ and $L^2(Y')$ to $L^2(X')$ respectively, then there exists a unique bounded linear transformation B, called the tensor product $A \otimes A'$ of A and A', that maps $L^2(Y \times Y')$ to $L^2(X \times X')$ so that if $v \in L^2(Y)$ and $v' \in L^2(Y')$, then*

(3) $\qquad B(v \otimes v') = Av \otimes A'v'.$

▶ If $w \in L^2(Y \times Y')$, then w induces a Hilbert-Schmidt operator $T(= \text{Int } w)$ from $L^2(Y')$ into $L^2(Y)$; the image of w under B is defined to be the kernel on $X \times X'$ that induces the Hilbert-Schmidt operator $AT(A')^*$. (It doesn't help to write this out formally, but, for the record, here is how the equation looks:

$$(A \otimes A')w = \text{Int}^{-1}(A(\text{Int } w)(A')^*).$$

The symbol "Int^{-1}" refers, of course, to the inverse of the one-to-one mapping Int from $L^2(X \times X')$ to Hilbert-Schmidt operators that map $L^2(X')$ to $L^2(X)$; cf. Theorem 8.1.)

Since A: $L^2(Y) \to L^2(X)$, T: $L^2(Y') \to L^2(Y)$, and $(A')^*$: $L^2(X') \to L^2(Y')$, the operator $AT(A')^*$ maps $L^2(X')$ to $L^2(X)$. That much is clear; but why is it a Hilbert-Schmidt operator?

Consider AT first; it maps $L^2(Y')$ to $L^2(X)$. If $\{g_j'\}$ is an orthonormal basis for $L^2(Y')$, then

$$\sum_j \|ATg_j'\|^2 \leqq \sum_j \|A\|^2 \cdot \|Tg_j'\|^2 = \|A\|^2 \cdot \|w\|_2^2$$

(by Theorem 4.5); this proves that AT is a Hilbert-Schmidt operator and that, moreover, the norm of the kernel that induces it ($\text{Int}^{-1}(AT)$) is dominated by $\|A\| \cdot \|w\|_2$.

The preceding paragraph proves that any left multiple (by, say, A) of any Hilbert-Schmidt operator (such as T) is a Hilbert-Schmidt operator again, and, moreover, that the passage from the inducing kernel of T to that of AT is bounded by $\|A\|$. The same is true of right multiples. To prove that, note that the adjoint of a Hilbert-Schmidt operator is the Hilbert-Schmidt operator induced by the conjugate transpose kernel (Theorem 7.5). Apply both the left and the right results to the product $AT(A')^*$ and conclude that

(4) $$\|A \otimes A'\| \leq \|A\| \cdot \|A'\|.$$

Consideration of tensor products $v \otimes v'$ shows that, in fact, equality holds in (4).[19]

The linearity of the transformation $A \otimes A'$ is obvious. Since finite linear combinations of tensor products such as $v \otimes v'$ are dense in $L^2(Y \times Y')$, uniqueness is a consequence of (3) and the validity of (2) for such tensor products. ◄

Note that if the definition of tensor product via Hilbert-Schmidt operators is accepted for Hilbert spaces that do not come presented as L^2 spaces, then the proof just given works just as well for them.

What is the relation between the tensor product of kernels and the tensor product of their induced operators? The answers are far from fully known.

Problem 9.4. ► *Is the tensor product of bounded kernels a bounded kernel? If k and k' are bounded kernels, is the tensor product operator $(\text{Int } k) \otimes (\text{Int } k')$ necessarily an integral operator? If the tensor product of two integral operators is an integral operator, $(\text{Int } k) \otimes (\text{Int } k') = \text{Int } h$, does it follow that $h = k \otimes k'$?* ◄

Even the little that is known is useful and is worth recording.

Theorem 9.5. *If k and k' are bounded kernels such that $k \otimes k'$ is a bounded kernel, then*
$$\text{Int}(k \otimes k') = (\text{Int } k) \otimes (\text{Int } k').$$

► If $g \in L^2(Y)$ and $g' \in L^2(Y')$, then, by Fubini's theorem,
$$\iint k(x, y) k'(x', y') g(y) g'(y') \, dy \, dy'$$
$$= (\int k(x, y) g(y) \, dy)(\int k'(x', y') g'(y') \, dy'),$$

so that $\text{Int}(k \otimes k')$ agrees with $(\text{Int } k) \otimes (\text{Int } k')$ on tensor products, and therefore everywhere. ◄

Theorem 9.6. *If k is a bounded kernel on $X \times Y$ and $k' = u' \otimes v'$ is a bounded kernel of rank 1 on $X' \times Y'$, then $k \otimes k'$ is a bounded kernel on $(X \times X') \times (Y \times Y')$.*

▶ The proof is a straightforward verification that $\mathrm{dom}(k \otimes k') = L^2(Y \times Y')$ (cf. Theorem 3.11 and the definition of domain).

(1) If $g \in L^2(Y \times Y')$, then

$$\iint |k(x,y)\,u'(x')\,\overline{v'(y')}\,g(y,y')|\,dy\,dy'$$
$$\leqq \int |k(x,y)\,u'(x')| \cdot \left(\sqrt{\int |v'(y')|^2\,dy'}\,\sqrt{\int |g(y,y')|^2\,dy'}\right)dy$$
$$= |u'(x')| \cdot \|v'\| \int |k(x,y)|\sqrt{\int |g(y,y')|^2\,dy'}\,|\,dy.$$

Since $\int |g(y,y')|^2\,dy'$, as a function of y, is in $L^2(Y)$ (because $g \in L^2(Y \times Y')$), the boundedness of k implies that the last-written expression is finite for almost every $\langle x, x' \rangle$, i.e., that

$$(k \otimes k')(\langle x, x' \rangle, \langle \cdot, \cdot \rangle)\,g \in L^1(Y \times Y')$$

for almost every $\langle x, x' \rangle$. (This part of the proof does not use the assumption that rank $k' = 1$; it works for any square integrable function in the role of k'.)

(2) Since $v' \in L^2(Y')$ and $g(y, \cdot) \in L^2(Y')$ for almost every y, and since

$$\int |\int \overline{v'(y')}\,g(y,y')\,dy'|^2\,dy$$
$$\leqq \int (\int |v'(y')|^2\,dy' \cdot \int |g(y,y')|^2\,dy')\,dy$$
$$= \|v'\|^2 \cdot \|g\|^2,$$

it follows that the integral $\int \overline{v'(y')}\,g(y,y')\,dy'$, as a function of y, belongs to $L^2(Y)$. The boundedness of k implies that

$$\int k(x,y)(\int \overline{v'(y')}\,g(y,y')\,dy')\,dy,$$

as a function of x, belongs to $L^2(X)$. Consequence: the transform

$$\iint k(x,y)\,u'(x')\,\overline{v'(y')}\,g(y,y')\,dy\,dy',$$

as a function of $\langle x, x' \rangle$, belongs to $L^2(X \times X')$. ◀

Example 9.7. Can an integral operator on $L^2(\mathbb{I})$ be an isometry? The emphasis is that both X and Y are $\mathbb{I}$, a space whose measure is finite and divisible. If Y is allowed to be infinite and atomic, then the discrete Fourier transform (Example 5.8) gives the affirmative answer. The answer to the present question is affirmative also, and the technique is the same as in §6: inflation and isomorphism. The inflation step can be viewed as an application of Theorem 9.6.

▶ For the first step, define k on $\mathbb{Z} \times \mathbb{I}$ by $k(n,y) = e^{-2\pi i n y}$, define k' on $\mathbb{I} \times \mathbb{Z}_1$ by $k'(x,1) = 1$, and form the tensor product $k \otimes k'$. Since $\mathrm{Int}\,k$ and $\mathrm{Int}\,k'$ are isometries (($\mathrm{Int}\,k'$) maps the constant α on $\mathbb{Z}_1$ onto the constant α on $\mathbb{I}$), it follows that $\mathrm{Int}(k \otimes k')$ is an isometry from $L^2(\mathbb{I} \times \mathbb{Z}_1)$ (which it is natural to identify with $L^2(\mathbb{I})$) into $L^2(\mathbb{Z} \times \mathbb{I})$ (which it is natural to identify with $L^2(\mathbb{R})$). Alternatively, the direct verification that $\mathrm{Int}(k \otimes k')$ is isometric is straightforward. (If $g \in L^2(\mathbb{I} \times \mathbb{Z}_1)$ and

$$f(n, x') = \iint (k \otimes k')(\langle n, x' \rangle, \langle y, 1 \rangle) g(y, 1) \, dy \, d1$$
$$= \int e^{-2\pi i n y} g(y, 1) \, dy,$$

then

$$\iint |f(n, x')|^2 \, dn \, dx' = \sum_n |\int e^{-2\pi i n y} g(y, 1) \, dy|^2 = \|g\|^2.)$$

The range of $\text{Int}(k \otimes k')$ regarded as a transformation from $L^2(\mathbb{I})$ to $L^2(\mathbb{R})$ is the set of all those functions in $L^2(\mathbb{R})$ that are constant in each unit interval $(n, n+1)$.

The second step, the transplanting of the measure of $\mathbb{R}$ into $\mathbb{I}$, can be achieved by a measure-theoretic isomorphism φ from $\mathbb{I}$ to $\mathbb{R}$. A possible φ is defined by

$$\varphi(x) = \log |\log x|. \quad \blacktriangleleft$$

Example 9.8. ▶ The inflation of a bounded matrix (on $\mathbb{Z}_+ \times \mathbb{Z}_+$) to a kernel (on $\mathbb{R}_+ \times \mathbb{R}_+$) is always bounded. Reason: inflating k is the same as forming the tensor product of k with the kernel k' on $\mathbb{I} \times \mathbb{I}$ defined by $k'(x, y) = 1$ for all $\langle x', y' \rangle$. It follows (Theorem 9.5) that inflating a bounded matrix has the same effect as forming the tensor product of an operator with a projection of rank 1. Note that the general theory of tensor products makes unnecessary the special boundedness proof in Example 5.1. ◀

Theorem 9.9. *The tensor product of bounded matrices is bounded.*

▶ The reason is that over an atomic space every operator is an integral operator. To be more explicit, suppose that a and b are bounded matrices and write $A = \text{Int } a$, $B = \text{Int } b$, $C = A \otimes B$. If $\{f_i\}$ and $\{g_j\}$ are the natural bases (so that $a(i, j) = (Af_j, f_i)$, $b(p, q) = (Bg_q, g_p)$), then the vectors $f_i \otimes g_p$ form an orthonormal basis for the tensor product space. (The conventions about the use of dashes are awkward here; it seems preferable to use distinct letters.) The proof is completed by computing the matrix c of C with respect to that basis, as follows:

$$c(\langle i, p \rangle, \langle j, q \rangle) = ((A \otimes B)(f_j \otimes g_q), (f_i \otimes g_p))$$
$$= (Af_j \otimes Bg_q, f_i \otimes g_p) = (Af_j, f_i)(Bg_q, g_p)$$
$$= a(i, j) b(p, q) = (a \otimes b)(\langle i, p \rangle, \langle j, q \rangle). \quad \blacktriangleleft$$

A kernel is a function on a Cartesian product; a naturally associated concept is that of a *subkernel*, that is, the restriction of the function to a smaller Cartesian product. Explicitly: if k is a kernel on $X \times Y$, and if X_0 and Y_0 are measurable subsets of X and Y, then the corresponding subkernel is the restriction k_0 of k to $X_0 \times Y_0$. (Cf. Theorem B1.) The obvious question has an easy answer: every subkernel of a bounded kernel is bounded. To prove this, observe first that the set Y_0 is a measure space in a natural way: its measurable subsets are the ones of the form $Y_0 \cap G$, where G is measurable in Y, and a measure v_0 is defined for such sets just by restricting v to them. If $g_0 \in L^2(Y_0)$, then extend g_0 to a function g in $L^2(Y)$ by setting g equal to 0 outside Y_0; if $f(x) = \int k(x, y) g(y) dy$, then $f \in L^2(X)$, and, therefore, the restriction f_0 of f to X_0 is in $L^2(X_0)$. Since

$$f_0(x) = \int k_0(x, y) g_0(y) dy$$

whenever $x \in X_0$, the boundedness of k_0 is proved. The integral operator $\text{Int } k_0$ may be called a *compression* of $\text{Int } k$.

The boundedness of tensor products and the boundedness of subkernels combine to yield another useful boundedness result.

Corollary 9.10. *If a and b are bounded matrices and if p is their Schur product $(p(i, j) = a(i, j) b(i, j))$, then p is a bounded matrix.*

▶ By Theorem 9.9, the tensor product c of a and b is a bounded matrix. Since the domain of c consists of ordered pairs of ordered pairs, one way to get a submatrix of c is to restrict both its arguments to the "diagonal". Since

$$c(\langle i, p\rangle, \langle j, q\rangle) = a(i, j) b(p, q),$$

the restriction of c to the set

$$\{\langle\langle i, p\rangle, \langle j, q\rangle\rangle : p = i, q = j\}$$

is exactly the Schur product. ◀

Note that the Schur product of two kernels can sometimes be bounded even if one of the factors is not. A trivial example is given by an arbitrary bounded kernel h and the kernel k defined by $k(x, y) = 1$ for all x and y. The Schur product of h and k is bounded because it is equal to h, but, unless the measures in both X and Y are finite, the kernel k is not bounded.

Example 9.11. If h is an arbitrary bounded kernel on $X \times Y$ and if the kernel k is defined on $X \times Y$ by $k(x, y) = \varphi(x) \psi(y)$, where $\varphi \in L^\infty(X)$ and $\psi \in L^\infty(Y)$, then the Schur product p defined by $p(x, y) = h(x, y) k(x, y)$ is bounded. (Note that the example in which k is identically equal to 1 is a special case.) If M_φ is the multiplication operator defined by $M_\varphi f = \varphi f$ for each f in $L^2(X)$, and, similarly, M_ψ is the multiplication operator induced by ψ on $L^2(Y)$, then $\text{Int } p = M_\varphi (\text{Int } h) M_\psi$.

▶ If $g \in L^2(Y)$, then $p(x, \cdot) g = h(x, \cdot) \varphi(x) \psi g = h(x, \cdot) \varphi(x) M_\psi g$; since $M_\psi g \in L^2(Y)$, the boundedness of h implies that $p(x, \cdot) g \in L^1(Y)$ for almost every x. To complete the proof, integrate:

$$\int h(x, y) \varphi(x) \psi(y) g(y) dy = \varphi(x)(\text{Int } h) M_\psi g(x),$$

and note that the result, as a function of x, belongs to $L^2(X)$. ◀[20]

§10. Absolute Boundedness

It is natural to ask "when is a kernel bounded?" Everyone does, and, sooner or later, everyone gives up. There is no good answer, and, in a sense, there cannot be one. Intuition seems to suggest that boundedness is a question of size: to be bounded is to be "small", or in any event not too large, and every kernel that is smaller than a bounded one is itself bounded. Since kernels are complex-valued functions, "size" presumably refers to absolute value. These vague and heuristic comments lead to at least one specific and precise question: is it true that if k and k' are kernels, k' is bounded, and $|k(x, y)| \leq |k'(x, y)|$ almost everywhere, then k is bounded?

The questions (and the answers) are reminiscent of the theory of infinite series. When is a series convergent? If a series is "smaller" than a convergent one, is it itself convergent? The facts for series are well known and discouraging. There is no usable necessary and sufficient condition for the convergence of a series; the definition of convergence is what it is, and nothing more efficient is known to be equivalent to it. As for domination: the alternating harmonic series $\left(\sum_n (-1)^n \frac{1}{n} \right)$ is convergent, but the "smaller" series obtained from it by replacing the positive terms by 0's is not. The source of the trouble has a name: the series is not absolutely convergent. The existence of a convergent series $\sum_n a_n$ for which the corresponding absolute series $\sum_n |a_n|$ is not convergent ruins all hope of finding a convergence test based on size.

A kernel k is *absolutely bounded* if the kernel $|k|$ is bounded. Most kernels in real life are absolutely bounded, and all absolutely bounded kernels are bounded. (This is a consequence of the corresponding elementary property of Lebesgue integration: a measurable function is integrable if and only if its absolute value is integrable.) The non-trivial question along these lines is whether any distinction exists at all: does there exist a bounded kernel that is not absolutely bounded? If so, then there is no hope of finding a boundedness test based on size.

A quick glance at the examples of Sections 4 and 5 is encouraging at first. A kernel is square integrable (Example 4.1) if and only if its absolute value is square integrable; every such kernel is not only bounded but automatically absolutely bounded. The projection kernel (Example 5.1), the Abel vibrating string kernel (Example 5.3), and the continuous Cesàro kernel (Example 5.4) are all positive, so that boundedness for them is the same as absolute boundedness.

What happens in the atomic case? Is there a bounded matrix a such that the corresponding absolute matrix $|a|$ $(|a|(i,j)=|a(i,j)|)$ is not bounded? The answer is yes, and that answer, at the same time as it shuts out a naive hope, opens the door to an extensive and useful theory.

Example 10.1. The first non-obvious class of examples is the class of Toeplitz matrices, and a relatively simple one among them that is only conditionally bounded is the Hilbert-Toeplitz matrix (Example 5.7).

▶ If k is that matrix, there are at least two ways to prove that $|k|$ is not bounded. One is to compute the function φ whose n-th Fourier coefficient α_n is given by

$$\alpha_n = \begin{cases} \dfrac{1}{|n|} & \text{for } n \neq 0, \\[2mm] 0 & \text{for } n = 0 \end{cases}$$

where $n = 0, \pm 1, \pm 2, \dots$. The result is

$$\varphi(x) = -\log|1 - e^{2\pi i x}|^2;$$

since φ is not bounded, $|k|$ is not bounded.

Another, longer but easier method is to prove that the matrix

$$h = \begin{pmatrix} 0 & 0 & 0 & 0 \\ 1 & 0 & 0 & 0 \\ \frac{1}{2} & 1 & 0 & 0 \\ \frac{1}{3} & \frac{1}{2} & 1 & 0 \\ & & & & \ddots \end{pmatrix}$$

is not bounded. (If $|k|$ were bounded, then $\frac{1}{2}(k+|k|)$ would be.) The most elementary way to do that is to exhibit a sequence $\{g_n\}$ of unit vectors in ℓ^2 such that the norms of the vectors of the transformed sequence become infinite. For this purpose, let g_n be the vector that has its first n coordinates equal to $1/\sqrt{n}$ $(n=1,2,3,\dots)$ and all others equal to 0. The first $n+1$ coordinates of the transform of g_n by h are

$$0, \frac{1}{\sqrt{n}}, \frac{1}{\sqrt{n}}\left(1+\frac{1}{2}\right), \dots, \frac{1}{\sqrt{n}}\left(1+\frac{1}{2}+\cdots+\frac{1}{n}\right).$$

It follows that the square of the norm of the transform of g_n is greater than or equal to

$$\frac{1}{n}(s_1 + \cdots + s_n),$$

where

$$S_m = \left(\sum_{j=1}^{m} \frac{1}{j} \right)^2.$$

Since $s_m \to \infty$ as $m \to \infty$, the same is true of the average of the s_m's. ◀ [21]

Example 10.2. ▶ The discrete Fourier transform (Example 5.8) is another example of a kernel that is only conditionally bounded. Indeed, since $|k(n, y)| = |e^{-2\pi i n y}| = 1$ for all n and all y, it follows that if $g \in L^2(\mathbb{I})$, then the transform

$$f(n) = \int |k(n, y)| g(y) \, dy = \int g(y) \, dy$$

is a constant function of n and, consequently, belongs to $L^2(\mathbb{Z})$ only in case the constant happens to be 0. ◀

What can be said about the integral operators whose kernels are not absolutely bounded? How widespread can the phenomenon be? Could it, for instance, happen with a compact integral operator? Even the faint hope that the very posing of the question raises is destined to be dashed. Yes, compact integral operators can have non-absolutely bounded kernels.

Example 10.3. ▶ For each positive integer n, let ω_n be a primitive n-th root of unity (that is, $\omega_n^n = 1$ but $\omega_n^p \neq 1$ when $0 < p < n$), and let w_n be the $n \times n$ matrix whose $\langle i, j \rangle$ entry is ω_n^{ij}. The $\langle i, j \rangle$ entry of the adjoint w_n^* is, of course, ω_n^{-ij}. It follows that the $\langle i, j \rangle$ entry of $w_n w_n^*$ is $\sum_p \omega_n^{(i-j)p}$. If $i = j$, this equals n; if $i \neq j$, then ω_n^{i-j} is an n-th root of 1 other than 1, and therefore the sum of its powers (from 0 to $n-1$) vanishes. Consequence: $w_n w_n^* = n$ ($= n$ times the identity matrix), so that the matrix $\frac{1}{\sqrt{n}} w_n$ is unitary, and hence $\|w_n\| = \sqrt{n}$.

The matrix $|w_n|$ whose entries are the absolute values of the entries of w_n has all its entries equal to 1. Since $\frac{1}{n} |w_n|$ is a projection, therefore $\| |w_n| \| = n$.

The direct sum

$$w = \sum_n \oplus (w_n / \sqrt{n}) = \begin{pmatrix} w_1 & & & \\ & w_2/\sqrt{2} & & \\ & & w_3/\sqrt{3} & \\ & & & \ddots \end{pmatrix}$$

of the matrices $\frac{1}{\sqrt{n}} w_n$ is unitary; the corresponding absolute matrix $|w|$ is unbounded. This proves only that w is bounded but not absolutely bounded (and thus, incidentally, gives an example of conditional boundedness that is more elementary than the Hilbert-Toeplitz matrix). To get a compact example, modify the construction as follows.

Since $\|w_n\|/n^{3/4} = 1/n^{1/4}$, the direct sum of the matrices $w_n/n^{3/4}$ is compact (the norms of the diagonal blocks tend to 0); since $\| |w_n| \|/n^{3/4} = n^{1/4}$, the corresponding absolute matrix is unbounded. This shows that absolute unboundedness can happen for compact matrices also.

It is instructive to observe that if a is a matrix of size n, then

$$\| |a| \| \leq \sqrt{n} \, \|a\|.$$

For the proof, recall the relation

$$\|a\| \leq \|a\|_2 \leq \sqrt{n} \, \|a\|$$

between the (operator) norm and the Hilbert-Schmidt norm of the kernel a (cf. Lemma 4.1). This relation implies that

$$\| |a| \| \leq \| |a| \|_2 = \|a\|_2 \leq \sqrt{n} \, \|a\|.$$

The example w_n shows that the upper bound $\sqrt{n}$ is attained for each n.

The example w_n is not as ad hoc as it might seem; many of its properties are forced by what is wanted. The facts constitute an interesting and useful bit of linear algebra; they can be stated as follows.

(1) If A is an operator and f is a unit vector, then a necessary and sufficient condition that A attain its norm at f (i.e., that $\|Af\| = \|A\|$) is that f be an eigenvector of A^*A with the eigenvalue $\|A\|^2$. (This is a folk-lemma. The proof depends on the condition for the Schwarz inequality to become an equation.)

(2) A necessary and sufficient condition that $\|a\| = \|a\|_2$ is that a be a dyad (i.e., rank $a \leq 1$, or, equivalently, $a(i,j) = \beta_i \gamma_j$ for some scalars β and γ). (For necessity use (1); for sufficiency observe that if A is a dyad, i.e., if $Af = (f,v)u$, then $\|A\| = \|u\| \cdot \|v\|$.)

The preceding two comments are true in general; the next two apply to matrices of size n.

(3) A necessary and sufficient condition that $\|a\|_2 = \sqrt{n} \, \|a\|$ is that a be a scalar multiple of a unitary matrix. (For necessity note that each column of a must have norm $\|a\|$ and then use (1); for sufficiency use the equation $\|a\|_2^2 = \operatorname{trace}(a^*a)$.)

(4) If $\| |a| \| = \sqrt{n} \, \|a\|$, then a is a scalar multiple of a unitary matrix and $|a(i,j)| = \|a\|/\sqrt{n}$ for all i and j. (Use (2) and (3) and observe that if $|a(i,j)| = \beta_i \gamma_j$, then the norm of the i-th row of a is $|\beta_i| \cdot (\sum_j |\gamma_j|^2)^{\frac{1}{2}}$ and the norm of the j-th column of a is $|\gamma_j| \cdot (\sum_i |\beta_i|^2)^{\frac{1}{2}}$.) ◀²²

Kernels behave differently on atomic and on divisible measure spaces. The preceding examples answer the existence question for bounded but not absolutely bounded kernels, but they leave open the possibility that that can happen only in the presence of atoms and infinite measures. Not so: non-absolute boundedness is consistent with divisibility and with finite measure; all that is needed is an easy application of the technique of inflation and change of measure.

Example 10.4. ▶ If a matrix a is inflated to a kernel k on $\mathbb{R}_+ \times \mathbb{R}_+$, and if a is bounded, then so is k. It follows that if a is *not* absolutely bounded, then neither is k. Indeed, if

$$\sum_i |\sum_j |a(i,j)| g(j)|^2$$

can be made arbitrarily large by appropriate choice of a unit vector g, then the action of $|k|$ on $g \otimes 1$ (the function whose value between n and $n+1$ is the constant $g(n)$) will produce just as large a norm. Consequence: the inflation of the Hilbert-Toeplitz matrix to a kernel on $\mathbb{R}_+ \times \mathbb{R}_+$ is bounded but not absolutely bounded. The same technique proves that the inflation of the discrete Fourier transform to a kernel on $\mathbb{R} \times \mathbb{I}$ is bounded but not absolutely bounded.

The result so far says that in certain cases if a tensor product $k \otimes k'$ is absolutely bounded, then so is k. The converse is also true sometimes. If, that is, a kernel k on $X \times Y$ is absolutely bounded, and if k' on $X' \times Y'$ is given by

$$k'(x', y') = u(x') \overline{v(x')}$$

with $u \in L^2(X')$, $v \in L^2(Y')$, then the tensor product $k \otimes k'$ is absolutely bounded. Proof: replace k, u, v by $|k|, |u|, |v|$, and apply Theorem 9.6 to infer that $|k| \otimes |k'|$ is absolutely bounded.

The isomorphism theorem yields conditionally bounded kernels over divisible spaces; all that is needed is to observe that Wk (in the notation of Theorem 6.2) is absolutely bounded if and only if k is. Proof: apply Theorem 6.1 to $|k|$ in place of k. ◀

The set of absolutely bounded kernels is algebraically well behaved. Some parts of that statement (e.g., that linear combinations of absolutely bounded kernels are absolutely bounded) are obvious from the definition; for others the following characterization of absolute boundedness is useful.

Theorem 10.5. *A kernel k on $X \times Y$ is absolutely bounded if and only if $\iint |f(x) k(x, y) g(y)| \, dx \, dy < \infty$ whenever $f \in L^2(X)$ and $g \in L^2(Y)$.*

▶ The "only if" is immediate from the definition of absolute boundedness.

Suppose conversely that the condition is satisfied. Assertion: if $g \in L^2(Y)$, then $k(x, \cdot) g \in L^1(Y)$ for almost every x. Reason: σ-finiteness implies the existence of an f in $L^2(X)$ such that $f(x) \neq 0$ for almost every x. Once such an f is fixed, the function h on $X \times Y$ defined by

$$h(x, y) = f(x) k(x, y) g(y)$$

belongs to $L^1(X \times Y)$ whenever g belongs to $L^2(Y)$. It follows that $h(x, \cdot) \in L^1(Y)$ for almost every x. Since division by $f(x)$ is permissible almost everywhere, the assertion follows.

The preceding paragraph shows that $Ag(x) = \int |k(x, y)| g(y) \, dy$ can almost always be formed (if $g \in L^2(Y)$); the next assertion is that $Ag \in L^2(X)$. The reason is that every product $f \cdot Ag$, with $f \in L^2(X)$, belongs to $L^1(X)$. Indeed:

$$\int |f(x) Ag(x)| \, dx \leq \iint |f(x) k(x, y) g(y)| \, dy \, dx,$$

which is finite by assumption.

The desired conclusion (that $|k|$ is a bounded kernel) follows from Theorem 3.11. ◄

Recall that if $f \in L^2(X)$ and $g \in L^2(Y)$, and if

$$(f \otimes g)(x, y) = f(x)\overline{g(y)},$$

then

$$f \otimes g \in L^2(X \times Y).$$

The condition of Theorem 10.5 is that every product of the form $k \cdot (f \otimes g)$ be integrable. The more restrictive condition that $k \cdot p$ be integrable whenever $p \in L^2(X \times Y)$ says exactly that $k \in L^2(X \times Y)$, i.e., that k is a square integrable kernel. There is a big difference between saying that $k \cdot p$ is integrable for all square integrable p and that it is integrable whenever p is a square integrable "dyad" (i.e., $p = f \otimes g$ with f and g square integrable).

Corollary 10.6. *If k is an absolutely bounded kernel, then k^* is an absolutely bounded kernel and $\operatorname{Int} k^* = (\operatorname{Int} k)^*$.*

▶ The absolute boundedness of k^* follows from that of k via Theorem 10.5; the asserted equation then follows from Theorem 7.5. ◄

Theorem 10.7. *If h and k are absolutely bounded kernels, on $X \times Y$ and $Y \times Z$ respectively, then $h(x, \cdot)k(\cdot, z) \in L^1(Y)$ for almost every $\langle x, z \rangle$. If ℓ is the convolution of h and k, then ℓ is an absolutely bounded kernel on $X \times Z$ and $\operatorname{Int} \ell = \operatorname{Int} h \cdot \operatorname{Int} k$.*

▶ The statement solves Problem 7.1 in the absolutely bounded case.

Since, for every g in $L^2(Z)$,

$$\int |k(y, z) g(z)| \, dz \in L^2(Y),$$

as a function of y, it follows that

(1) $\qquad \int |h(x, y)| (\int |k(y, z) g(z)| \, dz) \, dy \in L^2(X),$

as a function of x. If, moreover, $f \in L^2(X)$, then

(2) $\qquad \int |f(x)| (\int |h(x, y)| (\int |k(y, z) g(z)| \, dz) \, dy) \, dx < \infty,$

and therefore the function

$$\langle x, z \rangle \mapsto \int |f(x)| \cdot |h(x, y)| \cdot |k(y, z)| \cdot |g(z)| \, dy$$

is measurable, finite almost everywhere, and, in fact, in $L^1(X \times Z)$. It follows that if $f = \chi_F$ and $g = \chi_G$, where F and G are sets of finite measure, then

$$\langle x, z \rangle \mapsto \int |h(x, y) k(y, z)| \, dy$$

is measurable and finite almost everywhere in $F \times G$. Since F and G are arbitrary, σ-finiteness implies that

$$h(x, \cdot) k(\cdot, z) \in L^1(Y)$$

for almost every $\langle x, z \rangle$. It follows also that if $p(x, z) = \int h(x, y) k(y, z) \, dy$, then p is measurable, so that p is a kernel on $X \times Z$.

Now suppose, again, that g is an arbitrary element of $L^2(Z)$. Since

$$\int |p(x, z)| \cdot |g(z)| \, dz = \int |\int h(x, y) k(y, z) \, dy| \cdot |g(z)| \, dz$$
$$\leq \int (\int |h(x, y) k(y, z)| \, dy) \cdot |g(z)| \, dz$$
$$= \int |h(x, y)| (\int |k(y, z)| \cdot |g(z)| \, dz) \, dy,$$

and since, by (1), the last expression defines an element of $L^2(X)$, it follows via Theorem 10.5 that p is absolutely bounded.

The product formula follows from the finiteness of the triple integral (cf. (2)) via Fubini's theorem. ◀ [23]

The proof of the next theorem is further evidence that absolutely bounded kernels are pleasantly tractable. The result foreshadows a deeper one (with the same conclusion, but for all bounded kernels, not just for absolutely bounded ones), but the proof for the absolutely bounded case is easy and quick: it is one more application of the Riemann-Lebesgue technique (cf. Theorem 8.6).

Theorem 10.8. *If k is an absolutely bounded kernel on $\mathbb{I} \times \mathbb{I}$, then Int k is not invertible.*

▶ Let $\{e_n\}$ be the usual exponential basis for $L^2(\mathbb{I})$, and conclude (as in Theorem 8.6) that if $f_n = (\text{Int } k) e_n$, then $f_n(x) \to 0$ almost everywhere. Since, moreover,

$$|f_n(x)| = |\int k(x, y) e_n(y) \, dy| \leq \int |k(x, y)| \, dy,$$

and since the last integral, as a function of x, belongs to L^2 (because $e_0 \in L^2$ and $|k|$ is a bounded kernel), it follows from the Lebesgue dominated convergence theorem that $\|f_n\| \to 0$. That settles the matter: if an operator sends a sequence of unit vectors onto a null sequence, then it is not invertible. ◀

Four remarks. (1) Note that $k(x, \cdot) \in L^1$ even if the kernel k is only bounded (and not necessarily absolutely bounded), so that $\int |k(x, y)| \, dy$ makes sense and is finite for almost every x. Absolute boundedness was used to infer that the function of x so defined belongs to L^2. (2) Extensions to divisible spaces other than $\mathbb{I}$ are easily possible, just as for Theorem 8.6. (3) The proof proves more than the statement states. If an operator sends an orthonormal sequence onto a null sequence, then it has 0 not only in the spectrum but even in the so-called "essential spectrum"; the concept will be defined and discussed in §14. (4) Theorem 8.6 says, in particular, that $\|1 - \text{Int } k\| \geq 1$. Since $\|1 - \text{Int } k\| < 1$ would imply the invertibility of Int k, for absolutely bounded kernels this is an immediate consequence of Theorem 10.8.

Two more connections of the new concept (absolute boundedness) with the old ones remain to be examined: what can be said about direct sums and Schur products of absolutely bounded kernels?

As for direct sums: not much. The direct sum of absolutely bounded kernels can fail to be absolutely bounded even when it is bounded (see Example 10.3).

As for Schur products, there is at least one positive result that is worth a formal statement.

Theorem 10.9. *If h and k are (not necessarily bounded) kernels on $X \times Y$ such that $h(x, \cdot)$ and $k(x, \cdot)$ are in $L^2(Y)$ and have L^2 norms bounded by, say, α and β respectively, for almost every x, and $h(\cdot, y)$ and $k(\cdot, y)$ are in $L^2(X)$ and have L^2 norms bounded by α and β respectively, then the Schur product of h and k is absolutely bounded and the norm of the integral operator that the absolute kernel induces is bounded by $\alpha\beta$.*

▶ The Schur test (Theorem 5.2) is applicable, as follows:

$$\int |h(x, y) k(x, y)| \, dy \leq \sqrt{\int |h(x, y)|^2 \, dy} \, \sqrt{\int |k(x, y)|^2 \, dy} \leq \alpha\beta$$

and

$$\int |h(x, y) k(x, y)| \, dx \leq \sqrt{\int |h(x, y)|^2 \, dx} \, \sqrt{\int |k(x, y)|^2 \, dx} \leq \alpha\beta.$$

That is: in the present application the functions p and q of Theorem 5.2 are identically equal to 1, and the roles of both the constants α and β there are played by the present $\alpha\beta$. ◀ [24]

Note that Theorem 10.9 contains Corollary 9.10 as a special case. Indeed, if a is a bounded matrix and e_j is the characteristic function of $\{j\}$, then the j column of a is $(\text{Int } a)e_j$, so that the columns of a are in ℓ^2 and have ℓ^2 norms bounded by $\|a\|$; this result applied to a^* implies the same statement for rows.

The assertion of Theorem 10.9 for matrices is strictly stronger than that of Corollary 9.10; there do exist unbounded matrices with L^2 bounded rows and columns. One way to get one is to annihilate the upper triangle of the Hilbert-Toeplitz matrix; see Example 10.1.

Theorem 10.9 does not imply that Schur products can always be formed with impunity.

Example 10.10. ▶ The existence of non-absolutely bounded kernels shows that the Schur product of bounded kernels may fail to be bounded. Suppose indeed that h is a non-absolutely bounded (but bounded) kernel on $X \times Y$, where the measures in X and Y are finite. Write $k(x, y) = \text{sgn } \overline{h(x, y)}$ (where $\text{sgn } z = z/|z|$ or 0 according as $z \neq 0$ or $z = 0$). Since k is a bounded measurable function on a space of finite measure, it follows that k is a bounded (in fact absolutely bounded) kernel. Since, however, $h(x, y) k(x, y) = |h(x, y)|$, the Schur product of h and k is not bounded. ◀

The proof of Corollary 9.10, combined with the reasoning just given, does not imply that the tensor product of bounded kernels may become unbounded.

The reason is that, except in the atomic case, the diagonal set used in the proof of Corollary 9.10 is likely to have measure zero.

Remark 10.11. Example 10.4 exhibited an absolutely bounded tensor product $k \otimes k'$ and concluded that the factor k was also absolutely bounded. The phenomenon is general: if k (on $X \times Y$) and k' (on $X' \times Y'$) are kernels such that $k \otimes k'$ is absolutely bounded, and if k' is not the zero kernel (i.e., not almost everywhere equal to zero), then k is absolutely bounded.

▶ Since k' is not the zero kernel, $|k'|$ is pointwise bounded away from 0 (by α, say) on some set E of positive measure in $X' \times Y'$. Find f' in $L^2(X')$ and g' in $L^2(Y')$ so that

$$0 < \iint_E |f'(x')g'(y')| \, dx' \, dy' < \infty.$$

The absolute boundedness of k can be inferred from Theorem 10.5. Indeed, if $f \in L^2(X)$ and $g \in L^2(Y)$, then, by the absolute boundedness of the kernel $(k \otimes k')\chi_{X \times Y \times E}$, the "only if" of Theorem 10.5 implies that

$$\iint_E \iint_{X \times Y} |k(x, y) k'(x', y') f(x) f'(x') g(y) g'(y')| \, dx \, dy \, dx' \, dy' < \infty,$$

and hence that

$$(\alpha \iint_E |f'(x')g'(y')| \, dx' \, dy')(\iint |k(x, y) f(x) g(y)| \, dx \, dy) < \infty.$$

Since the first factor is positive, the second factor must be finite, and the "if" of Theorem 10.5 yields the conclusion. ◀

The moral of this section is that the class of absolutely bounded kernels, which is large enough for much interesting analysis, is small enough to exclude most of the pathology of the subject.

§11. Carleman Kernels

There is a sense in which the most natural integral operators on L^2 are the ones induced by Carleman kernels (the semi-square-integrable kernels k, for which $k(x, \cdot) \in L^2(Y)$ for almost every x).

If, to begin with, a matrix a is bounded, then each of its rows is square summable. The converse, by the way, is not true. (If it were, then there would be a simple "size" test for the boundedness of a matrix.) A simple counterexample is the matrix a defined by

$$a(i, j) = i\delta(i, j)$$

(where δ is, as usual, the characteristic function of the diagonal).

A small generalization of the positive assertion of the preceding paragraph says that if k is a bounded kernel on $X \times Y$, where the measure space X is atomic, then $k(x, \cdot) \in L^2(Y)$ for every x in X. (Cf. Theorem 7.3.) Is it necessary to assume that X is atomic? Here is a tempting proof that the answer is no, at least in the almost everywhere sense (which is all that can be expected). If k is bounded and $g \in L^2(Y)$, then $k(x, \cdot)g \in L^1(Y)$ for almost every x in X, so that $k(x, \cdot)$ multiplies $L^2(Y)$ into $L^1(Y)$ for almost every x. Conclusion: $k(x, \cdot) \in L^2(Y)$ for almost every x. The proof is wrong. What's wrong is this: it is true that if $g \in L^2(Y)$, then there exists a set $F(g)$ of measure zero in X such that $k(x, \cdot)g \in L^1(Y)$ whenever $x \notin F(g)$; but it does not follow that there is a set F of measure zero in X such that if $x \notin F$, then $k(x, \cdot)$ multiplies every g in $L^2(Y)$ into $L^1(Y)$. In other words: $F(g)$ may depend on g in a non-trivial manner; since there are many g's, it may turn out that too many sets of measure zero have to be thrown away.

Is every bounded kernel a Carleman kernel? A natural attempt to prove the implication turned out to be wrong, but is the implication right anyway? No, it is not, not even for absolutely bounded kernels.

Example 11.1. ▶ For each number s with $\frac{1}{2} \leq s < 1$ define a kernel k_s on $\mathbb{I} \times \mathbb{I}$ by

$$k_s(x, y) = \begin{cases} 0 & \text{if } x \leq y, \\ \dfrac{1}{(x - y)^s} & \text{if } x > y. \end{cases}$$

The Schur test can be used to prove that the kernels k_s are bounded, exactly as in Example 5.3; the computations go as follows:

$$\int_0^x \frac{dy}{(x - y)^s} = \int_0^1 \frac{x\,du}{x^s(1 - u)^s} = \frac{x^{1-s}}{1 - s} \leq \frac{1}{1 - s},$$

and

$$\int_y^1 \frac{dx}{(x-y)^s} = \int_1^{1/y} \frac{y\,du}{y^s(u-1)^s} = \frac{(1-y)^{1-s}}{1-s} \leqq \frac{1}{1-s}.$$

(Note the need for the assumption $s<1$.) Since

$$\int_0^1 |k_s(x, y)|^2\, dy = \int_0^x \frac{dy}{(x-y)^{2s}},$$

the assumption $s \geqq \frac{1}{2}$ implies that k_s is not a Carleman kernel. (For $s = \frac{1}{2}$ this example reduces to the Abel vibrating string kernel discussed in Example 5.3.)

Suppose now that s is temporarily fixed, $\frac{1}{2}<s<1$. (The case $s=\frac{1}{2}$ is exceptional.) Assertion: to each x in $\mathbb{I}$ there corresponds a function g_x in $L^2(\mathbb{I})$ such that $k_s(x, \cdot)g_x \notin L^1(\mathbb{I})$. To prove this, choose a number t with $1-s<t<\frac{1}{2}$, and write

$$g_x(y) = \begin{cases} 0 & \text{if } x \leqq y, \\ \dfrac{1}{(x-y)^t} & \text{if } x>y. \end{cases}$$

(Note that the interval $(1-s, \frac{1}{2})$ is non-degenerate exactly when $s>\frac{1}{2}$.) The assumption $t<\frac{1}{2}$ guarantees that $g_x \in L^2(\mathbb{I})$ for each x. Since, however,

$$k_s(x, y)\, g_x(y) = \begin{cases} 0 & \text{if } x \leqq y, \\ \dfrac{1}{(x-y)^{s+t}} & \text{if } x>y, \end{cases}$$

and since $s+t>1$, the product $k_s(x, \cdot)g_x$ is not in $L^1(\mathbb{I})$.

What does that prove? It proves that (once s is fixed) the bounded kernel k_s does not have the property that $k_s(x, \cdot)$ multiplies $L^2(\mathbb{I})$ into $L^1(\mathbb{I})$ for almost every x; *every* x meets at least one "bad" function g_x such that g_x is in $L^2(\mathbb{I})$ but $k_s(x, \cdot)g_x$ is not in $L^1(\mathbb{I})$. In other words: every x must belong to at least one bad set of measure zero (e.g., the one corresponding to g_x).

The Abel kernel $k_{1/2}$ behaves the same way as the k_s's with $s>\frac{1}{2}$, but the computations are slightly more cumbersome. For x in $\mathbb{I}$, write

$$g_x(y) = \begin{cases} 0 & \text{if } x \leqq y, \\ \dfrac{1}{\sqrt{x-y}\,(1-\log(x-y))} & \text{if } x>y. \end{cases}$$

Since

$$\int_0^x \frac{dy}{(x-y)(1-\log(x-y))^2} = \int_0^1 \frac{x\,du}{x(1-u)(1-\log x(1-u))^2}$$
$$= \int_{1-\log x}^{\infty} \frac{dv}{v^2} = \frac{1}{1-\log x},$$

it follows that $g_x \in L^2(\mathbb{I})$. Since, however,

$$\int_0^x \frac{1}{\sqrt{x-y}} \cdot \frac{dy}{\sqrt{x-y}\,(1-\log(x-y))} = \int_0^1 \frac{x\,du}{x(1-u)(1-\log x - \log(1-u))}$$

$$= \int_{1-\log x}^\infty \frac{dv}{v} = \infty,$$

the products $k_{1/2}(x,\,\cdot\,)g_x$ are not in $L^1(\mathbb{I})$ for any x.

The kernels k_s have an algebraic property that is frequently exploited: except for an easily computed normalizing factor, the convolution of k_s and k_t is k_{s+t-1}. For the proof, observe that $k_s(x,z)k_t(z,y)=0$ when $x \leq y$ (because in that case either $x \leq z$ or $z \leq y$); if $x > y$, replace z in the integral

$$\int_y^x \frac{dz}{(x-z)^s(z-y)^t}$$

by $ux+(1-u)y$. Application: the convolution of the Abel kernel ($s=\frac{1}{2}$) with itself is a constant multiple of the Volterra kernel (Example 4.2); correspondingly the operator induced by the Abel kernel is (except for a constant factor) a square root of indefinite integration (on $\mathbb{I}$). These remarks make contact with the theory of "fractional integration". ◀ [25]

The set $\mathscr{I} = \mathscr{I}(X, Y)$ of all bounded kernels on $X \times Y$ has three important subsets: the set $\mathscr{A} = \mathscr{A}(X,Y)$ of all absolutely bounded kernels, the set $\mathscr{C} = \mathscr{C}(X,Y)$ of all bounded Carleman kernels, and the set $\mathscr{L}^2 = \mathscr{L}^2(X,Y)$ of all square integrable kernels.

Theorem 11.2. *All the general inclusion relations among $\mathscr{A}$, $\mathscr{I}$, $\mathscr{C}$, and $\mathscr{L}^2$ are the ones indicated in the lattice diagram:*

▶ Explanation: $\mathscr{L}^2 \subset \mathscr{A} \cap \mathscr{C}$, $\mathscr{A} \cup \mathscr{C} \subset \mathscr{I}$; both inclusions are strict; and there exist Carleman kernels that are not absolutely bounded, and vice versa.

The inclusions $\mathscr{L}^2 \subset \mathscr{A}$ (Section 10) and $\mathscr{A} \subset \mathscr{I}$ (Section 10) were discussed before; the inclusions $\mathscr{C} \subset \mathscr{I}$ (definition) and $\mathscr{L}^2 \subset \mathscr{C}$ (Fubini's theorem) are trivial. The discrete Fourier transform is a bounded Carleman kernel that is not absolutely bounded (Example 10.2), and so is the Hilbert-Toeplitz matrix (Example 5.7, Example 10.1); the Abel kernel (Example 5.3, Example 11.1) is an absolutely bounded kernel that is not a Carleman kernel.

It remains to show that the *'s in the diagram are distinct from the top and the bottom. For the top, form the direct sum of a bounded Carleman kernel that is not absolutely bounded and an absolutely bounded kernel that is not a Carleman kernel. The result is a bounded kernel that is neither absolutely bounded nor a Carleman kernel. For the bottom, a trivial but adequate example is the identity matrix. ◄

Example 11.3. ► Since every bounded matrix is a Carleman kernel, some counterexamples cannot use atomic spaces. On the other hand, some of the examples used to prove Theorem 11.2 are based on atomic spaces: can that be avoided? Specifically: is there a bounded Carleman kernel on $\mathbb{I} \times \mathbb{I}$ that is not absolutely bounded, and is there an absolutely bounded Carleman kernel on $\mathbb{I} \times \mathbb{I}$ that is not square integrable? The answer is yes, and one way to get at it is to use, as before, the technique of inflation and isomorphism.

Consequences: yes, there is a conditionally bounded Carleman kernel on $\mathbb{I} \times \mathbb{I}$; and yes, there is an absolutely bounded Carleman kernel on $\mathbb{I} \times \mathbb{I}$ that is not square integrable; just inflate the examples is the proof of Theorem 11.2 and then apply isomorphisms to make the measures finite. ◄

It is sometimes illuminating to look at Carleman kernels from a point of view different from the one that motivated their introduction. To understand the alternative point of view, observe that a Carleman kernel k on $X \times Y$ induces a natural mapping, namely $x \mapsto k(x, \cdot)$, from the measure space X to the Hilbert space $L^2(Y)$. (If $k(x, \cdot) \notin L^2(Y)$ for certain x's, discard them.) The action of the operator $A = \text{Int}\, k$ can be nearly recaptured from that mapping in purely Hilbert space terms: if $g \in L^2(Y)$, then

$$A g(x) = \int k(x, y) g(y)\, dy = (g, \overline{k(x, \cdot)}).$$

The reason for the "nearly" is the presence of the complex conjugation. The sensible way out is to consider the mapping $x \mapsto \overline{k(x, \cdot)}$ instead; from it A *can* be recaptured using nothing but inner products. (The alternative of noting that $A g(x) = (k(x, \cdot), \bar{g})$ pushes the difficulty to a technically more awkward place.) That is: associated with every Carleman kernel k there is a function γ from X to $L^2(Y)$, defined by

$$\gamma(x) = \overline{k(x, \cdot)},$$

and the action of the induced operator is defined by

$$A g(x) = (g, \gamma(x)).$$

The function γ is weakly measurable in the usual sense that the function (g, γ) is measurable for each g. (Here (g, γ) is defined by $(g, \gamma)(x) = (g, \gamma(x))$.) More is true: if k is bounded, then the functions (g, γ) belong to $L^2(X)$ and the passage from g to (g, γ) is bounded, in the sense that there exists a positive constant M such that

$$\int |(g, \gamma(x))|^2\, dx \leq M^2 \|g\|^2$$

for all g. This is just a transcription to present notation of the definition of boundedness. [26]

These considerations motivate a general definition: a *Carleman function* is a weakly measurable function from a (separable, sigma-finite) measure space X to a (separable) Hilbert space K. The concept is more a reformulation than a generalization of the concept of Carleman kernel, but till the precise relation between the two is established, it is as well to treat the theory of Carleman functions respectfully, as an analogue of the theory of Carleman kernels.

The *domain* of a Carleman function $\gamma: X \to K$ is the set

$$\operatorname{dom} \gamma$$

of all those g in K for which the function (g, γ) is in $L^2(X)$. A Carleman function induces an operator, which may, by a mild abuse of notation, be denoted by

$$\operatorname{Int} \gamma;$$

it is the operator from $\operatorname{dom} \gamma$ into $L^2(X)$ defined by

$$(\operatorname{Int} \gamma) g(x) = (g, \gamma(x)).$$

Obviously $\operatorname{Int} \gamma$ is linear. It is not necessarily bounded, but it is always closed; the proof is exactly the same as the proof of Theorem 3.8 (which states that the integral operator induced by a Carleman kernel is always closed). It follows from the closed graph theorem that if a Carleman function γ has full domain ($\operatorname{dom} \gamma = K$), then $\operatorname{Int} \gamma$ is bounded; it is convenient to abbreviate this by saying that γ is bounded. In other words, a Carleman function γ is *bounded* if there exists a positive constant M such that

$$\int |(g, \gamma(x))|^2 \, dx \leq M^2 \|g\|^2$$

for all g in K.

Perhaps boundedness in the sense just defined should be called something more specific (such as "operator boundedness" or "L^2 boundedness"); there are at least two other concepts that deserve the name. A Carleman function γ is *strongly bounded* if there exists a positive constant M such that

$$\|\gamma(x)\| \leq M$$

for almost every x, and it is *weakly bounded* if there exists a positive constant M such that for each g in K the inequality

$$|(g, \gamma(x))| \leq M \|g\|$$

holds for almost every x.

The obvious relations among these concepts are these: every strongly bounded function is weakly bounded, and, if the measure in X is finite, then every weakly bounded function is (operator) bounded. The converse of the latter assertion is false, even for finite measure spaces: (operator) bounded Carleman functions may fail to be weakly bounded. One way to get a counterexample is to use the corresponding counterexample for Carleman kernels. (Example (4.2)): let u and v be unbounded functions in $L^2(X)$ and $L^2(Y)$ respectively, let k be the Carleman kernel $u \otimes v$, and define γ by $\gamma(x) = \overline{k(x, \cdot)}$. The kernel k is bounded of course (Int k is a Hilbert-Schmidt operator of rank 1), but γ is not weakly bounded. (If $g = v$, then $(g, \gamma(x)) = \int u(x)\overline{v(y)}\, v(y)\, dy = u(x)\|v\|^2$.) Note, however, that if $X = \mathbb{Z}$, then every (operator) bounded Carleman function is strongly bounded. Reason: $g \mapsto (g, \gamma(x))$ is a bounded linear functional on K, and $x \mapsto (g, \gamma(x))$ is a square integrable function on X. It follows that the latter is bounded for each g (square summable sequences are bounded), and the principle of uniform boundedness implies that the function $x \mapsto \|\gamma(x)\|$ is bounded.

Theorem 11.4. *Every weakly bounded Carleman function is strongly bounded.* [27]

▶ Given $\gamma: X \to K$, let $\{g_n\}$ be a countable set dense in K, and, for each n, let E_n be a set of measure zero in X such that if $x \notin E_n$, then $|(g_n, \gamma(x))| \leq M\|g_n\|$. (Here M is a constant whose existence the weak boundedness of γ guarantees.) Assertion: if $x \notin \bigcup_n E_n$, then $|(g, \gamma(x))| \leq M\|g\|$ for all g in K. (Indeed: find a sequence $\{g_{n_j}\}$ converging to g; note that

$$|(g, \gamma(x))| \leq |(g - g_{n_j}, \gamma(x))| + |(g_{n_j}, \gamma(x))|$$
$$\leq \|g - g_{n_j}\| \cdot \|\gamma(x)\| + M\|g_{n_j}\|;$$

as $j \to \infty$, with x still fixed, the first summand of the last expression tends to 0 and the second to $M\|g\|$; this proves the assertion.) Conclusion: if $x \notin \bigcup_n E_n$, then

$$\|\gamma(x)\| = \sup\{|(g, \gamma(x))|: \|g\| = 1\} \leq M. \quad ◀$$

After this digression into what boundedness could mean for Carleman functions, the terminology will be fixed according to the original definition: "bounded" will mean "operator bounded" and the other kind of boundedness (weak or strong) will be adjectivally identified whenever it is needed.

If K happens to be $L^2(Y)$, then one way to get a Carleman function $\gamma: X \to K$ is the way originally used to motivate the concept: let k be a Carleman kernel on $X \times Y$ and write $\gamma(x) = \overline{k(x, \cdot)}$. Is that the only way?

The question leads to some pathological measurability problems. Formally all seems clear. Given γ, and given x in X, form $\gamma(x)$; since $\gamma(x) \in L^2(Y)$, it has a value $(\gamma(x))(y)$ at each y; recalling the complex conjugation that inner products make necessary, set $k(x, y) = \overline{(\gamma(x))(y)}$.

There are two things wrong with this formal procedure. First, $\gamma(x)$ is not really a function, but an equivalence class of functions; the act of evaluating $\gamma(x)$ at y has to be replaced by finding a function in $\gamma(x)$ and evaluating that function at y. Second, the procedure involves, in general, uncountably many arbitrary choices, and does not therefore guarantee that the resulting function k on $X \times Y$ is measurable. Both these difficulties are real, but, fortunately, they can be made to go away.

Theorem 11.5. *Every bounded Carleman function from X to $L^2(Y)$ is induced by a bounded Carleman kernel on $X \times Y$.*[28]

▶ Let γ be a bounded Carleman function, $\gamma: X \to K$, and consider first the Hilbert-Schmidt case; that is, assume that $\|\gamma\| \in L^2(X)$. Let $\{e_n\}$ be a countable orthonormal basis for $L^2(X)$ and observe that, for every x,

$$\gamma(x) = \sum_n (\gamma(x), e_n) e_n,$$

and therefore

$$\|\gamma(x)\|^2 = \sum_n |(\gamma(x), e_n)|^2.$$

It follows that

$$\int \|\gamma(x)\|^2 \, dx = \int \sum_n |(\gamma(x), e_n)|^2 \, dx$$

$$= \sum_n \int |(\gamma(x), e_n)|^2 \, dx.$$

Since the left side is finite, so is the right, and, therefore, the partial sums of the last series form a Cauchy sequence.

For each n choose a function e_n^0 in the equivalence class of e_n, and write

$$k_n(x, y) = \sum_{j=1}^{n} (\gamma(x), e_j) e_j^0(y).$$

The function k_n is measurable (and square integrable) on $X \times Y$. Assertion: the sequence $\{k_n\}$ is a Cauchy sequence in $L^2(X \times Y)$. Indeed:

$$\|k_{n+m} - k_n\|^2 = \iint \left| \sum_{j=n+1}^{n+m} (\gamma(x), e_j) e_j^0(y) \right|^2 dx \, dy$$

$$= \int \left(\int \sum_{i=n+1}^{n+m} \sum_{j=n+1}^{n+m} (\gamma(x), e_i) e_i^0(y) \overline{(\gamma(x), e_j)} \, \overline{e_j^0(y)} \right) dy \, dx$$

$$= \int \left(\sum_{j=n+1}^{n+m} |(\gamma(x), e_j)|^2 \right) dx.$$

Hence, by the preceding paragraph and the completeness of $L^2(X \times Y)$, there exists a square integrable function k on $X \times Y$ such that $k_n \to k$ in $L^2(X \times Y)$. It follows that, for some subsequence of the sequence $\{k_n\}$ of kernels, the sections $k_n(x, \cdot)$ converge to $k(x, \cdot)$ in $L^2(Y)$ for almost every x. Since, however, by definition,

$$k_n(x, \cdot) \in \sum_{j=1}^{n} (\gamma(x), e_j) e_j,$$

(where the right side of this relation is viewed as an equivalence class), and since $\sum_{j=1}^{n} (\gamma(x), e_j) e_j \to \gamma(x)$ in $L^2(Y)$ (for almost every x), it follows that

$$k(x, \cdot) \in \gamma(x)$$

for almost every x; the proof for the Hilbert-Schmidt case is complete.

Turn now to the general case, where $\|\gamma\|$ is not assumed to be square integrable. Since X is σ-finite, there exists a measurable function φ on X that is strictly positive everywhere but small enough to guarantee that the function $\varphi\|\gamma\|$ is square integrable. (Decompose X into countably many sets of finite measure on each of which $\|\gamma\|$ is pointwise bounded, and let φ be a sufficiently small positive constant on each such set.) Write $\gamma'(x) = \varphi(x)\gamma(x)$ and apply the conclusion for the Hilbert-Schmidt case to find a measurable function k' such that $k'(x, \cdot) \in \gamma'(x)$ for almost every x. It follows that $k(x, \cdot) = \dfrac{1}{\varphi(x)} k'(x, \cdot) \in \gamma(x)$ almost everywhere, and the proof is complete. ◄

The mapping that associates with each bounded Carleman kernel k the bounded Carleman function γ defined by $\gamma(x) = \overline{k(x, \cdot)}$ is obviously conjugate linear and injective (if it is understood, as usual, that sets of measure zero are ignored); Theorem 11.5 shows that it is surjective.

The mapping $\gamma \mapsto \operatorname{Int} \gamma$ is equally obviously conjugate linear. The separability of K implies that it too is injective. Indeed: if $A = \operatorname{Int} \gamma = 0$, then, in particular, $A e_n = 0$ for each term e_n of a countable orthonormal basis for K. This implies that there exists a set E of measure zero such that if $x \notin E$, then $0 = A e_n(x) = (e_n, \gamma(x))$. Consequence: if $x \notin E$, then $\gamma(x) = 0$, i.e., $\gamma = 0$ almost everywhere. Since not every operator is an integral operator, and not every bounded kernel is a Carleman kernel, the mapping $\gamma \mapsto \operatorname{Int} \gamma$ is not, in general, surjective.

The multiplicative properties of Int are of considerably greater interest than its merely set-theoretic and linear ones; the next result concerns them.

Theorem 11.6. *If $\gamma: X \to K$ is a bounded Carleman function and $B: K \to K'$ is a bounded linear transformation, then the composition $\gamma' = B\gamma$ (that is, $\gamma'(x) = B(\gamma(x))$) is a bounded Carleman function from X to K', and $\operatorname{Int} \gamma' = (\operatorname{Int} \gamma) B^*)$.* [29]

► The assertion is that if an operator induced by a Carleman function (a *Carleman operator*) is multiplied *on the right* (i.e., preceded) by an arbitrary bounded linear transformation, the result is another such operator. In case $K' = K = L^2(X)$, the result can be expressed by saying that the set of all Carleman operators is a right ideal.

Now for the proof. If $g' \in K'$, then

$$(g', \gamma'(x)) = (g', B\gamma(x)) = (B^* g', \gamma(x)) = ((\operatorname{Int} \gamma) B^* g')(x),$$

so that γ' is weakly measurable. Since

$$\int |(g', \gamma'(x))|^2 \, dx = \int |(B^* g', \gamma(x))|^2 \, dx = \|(\operatorname{Int} \gamma) B^* g'\|^2,$$

it follows that γ' is bounded. Once this is known, so that $\operatorname{Int} \gamma'$ makes sense, then $(\operatorname{Int} \gamma') g'(x) = (g', \gamma'(x))$ is true by definition, and the equation asserted by the theorem is proved. ◄

Corollary 11.7. *A bounded Carleman operator on $L^2(\Pi)$ (or, for that matter, on $L^2(X)$ for any divisible space X) cannot be invertible (or even right invertible).*

▶ The identity operator is not a Carleman operator (see Theorem 8.5 or 8.6); the conclusion follows from Theorem 11.6.

Note that all that is needed for the proof is that not every operator on $L^2(X)$ is a Carleman operator. Once that is known, the right-ideal theorem (11.6) recaptures the result that the identity is not a Carleman operator, and implies, therefore, that no right invertible operator is a Carleman operator. ◀

Problem 11.8. ▶ It is natural to ask whether anything like the right-ideal theorem is true for integral operators that are not necessarily Carleman operators. *Is the set of all integral operators on $L^2(X)$ always a right ideal? More generally: if k is a bounded kernel on $X \times Y$ and if B is a bounded linear transformation from $L^2(Z)$ into $L^2(Y)$, does if follow that $(\mathrm{Int}\,k)B$ is an integral operator from $L^2(Z)$ into $L^2(X)$? What if k is absolutely bounded? Even if the set of all integral operators is not a right ideal, is it at least an algebra (i.e., is it closed under the formation of products)?* ◀

The conclusion of the present treatment of Carleman operators has to do with adjoints. The adjoint of an integral operator is sometimes an integral operator and sometimes not (cf. Example 7.2, Theorem 7.5, and Corollaries 7.6 and 7.7). In any event, the adjoint makes sense, and it is frustrating to deal with an "explicitly defined" operator (such as an integral operator) and not be able to define its adjoint equally explicitly. For Carleman operators this frustration can be avoided.

To understand the behavior of the adjoints of Carleman operators it is necessary to study a new aspect of Carleman functions, and to understand that, it is wise to take another look at the formalism of finite matrices. If

$$A g(i) = \sum_j a(i,j) g(j),$$

then

$$A^* f(j) = \sum_i \overline{a(i,j)} f(i).$$

In terms of Carleman functions, the first of these equations is the familiar statement $A g(x) = (g, \gamma(x))$. The second equation is different: it says that the image under A^* of a function f in $L^2(X)$ is obtained by using the values of f as "coefficients" to form a "linear combination" of the vectors $\gamma(x)$ in K.

What this suggests is that there are two ways to make operators out of Carleman functions, not one. Recall that a Carleman function was defined as a weakly measurable function γ from a measure space X to a Hilbert space K; the function γ is called bounded in case the mapping

$$g \to (g, \gamma)$$

is a bounded linear transformation from K to $L^2(X)$. There is a dual notion. Call the (weakly measurable) function γ *co-bounded* in case the mapping

$$f \mapsto \int f(x) \gamma(x)\,dx$$

defines a bounded linear transformation from $L^2(X)$ to K.

What can an integral such as $\int f(x)\gamma(x)dx$ mean? The simplest answer is to interpret it in the weak sense. That is: the equation

$$\int f\gamma \, d\mu = f'$$

(where $f' \in K$) means that for each vector g in K the product $f(x)(\gamma(x), g)$ is integrable over X (i.e., $f\gamma$ is weakly integrable), and

$$\int f(x)(\gamma(x), g)\, dx = (f', g).$$

(Note that this is formally fitting:

$$\int f(x)(\gamma(x), g)\, dx = (\int f(x)\gamma(x)\, dx, g).)$$

The requirement of co-boundedness is that the passage from f to f' be a bounded linear transformation. If that is true, the symbol

$$\text{Int}^* \, \gamma$$

will be used to denote that passage. (Just as for Int γ, in case $K = L^2(Y)$ and γ is induced by the kernel k on $X \times Y$, the operator Int$^* \gamma$ may be written as Int$^* k$.)

Theorem 11.9. *If γ is a weakly measurable function from a measure space X to a Hilbert space K, then a necessary and sufficient condition that γ be bounded is that it be co-bounded; if the condition is satisfied, then*

$$(\text{Int } \gamma)^* = \text{Int}^* \, \gamma.$$

▶ Suppose first that γ is bounded, and take f in $L^2(X)$, g in K. It follows that the function $x \mapsto (g, \gamma(x))$ is in $L^2(X)$, so that $x \mapsto f(x)(\gamma(x), g)$ is in $L^1(X)$. Since

$$\int f(x)(\gamma(x), g)\, dx = \int f(x)\overline{(g, \gamma(x))}\, dx$$
$$= (f, (\text{Int } \gamma)g),$$

the conjugate linear functional $g \mapsto \int f(x)(\gamma(x), g)\, dx$ is bounded. This means, by definition, that $f\gamma$ is weakly integrable. Since, moreover,

$$(\int f(x)\gamma(x)\, dx, g) = \int f(x)(\gamma(x), g)\, dx,$$

it follows that γ is co-bounded.

Suppose next that, conversely, γ is co-bounded. The weak integrability of $f\gamma$ implies that $f \cdot (g, \gamma)$ is in $L^1(X)$ for all g in K, and hence that $(g, \gamma) \in L^2(X)$. Since, moreover,

$$(f, (g, \gamma)) = \int f(x)(\gamma(x), g)\, dx$$
$$= (\int f(x)\gamma(x)\, dx, g)$$
$$= ((\text{Int}^* \, \gamma)\, f, g),$$

it follows that γ is bounded.

Comparison of the displayed equations in the preceding two paragraphs shows that

$$(\text{Int } \gamma)^* = \text{Int}^* \gamma,$$

and thus completes the proof. ◀

A typical example of Theorem 11.9 is the discrete Fourier transform, i.e., the kernel k on $\mathbb{Z} \times \mathbb{I}$ defined by

$$k(n, y) = e^{-2\pi i n y}.$$

The corresponding Carleman function $\gamma \colon \mathbb{Z} \to L^2(Y)$ is defined by

$$\gamma(n) = e^{2\pi i n \cdot}.$$

The adjoint of Int k (the compact Fourier transform) is, by Theorem 11.9, given by

$$(\text{Int } k)^* f = \sum_n f(n)\, \gamma(n)$$

(cf. Example 7.2). This "integral" (in the present case a sum) does not usually make pointwise sense:

$$\sum_n f(n)\, e^{2\pi i n x}$$

is an absolutely convergent series only if $f \in \ell^1$. By Theorem 11.9, however, it makes good "weak" sense.

The next assertion is not restricted to Carleman operators only, but it motivates the one that follows it, which is.

Theorem 11.10. *If k is a bounded kernel on $X \times X$, then a necessary and sufficient condition that Int k be Hermitian is that $k = k^*$.*

▶ If Int $k = (\text{Int } k)^*$, then $(\text{Int } k)^*$ is an integral operator, and, by Theorem 7.5, $(\text{Int } k)^* = \text{Int } k^*$; the equation $k = k^*$ follows from the uniqueness theorem (8.1). If, conversely, $k = k^*$, then, by Theorem 7.5, $(\text{Int } k)^* = \text{Int } k^* = \text{Int } k$. ◀

Normal operators are sometimes almost as well behaved as Hermitian ones; the following assertion is a case in point.

Theorem 11.11. *If k is a bounded Carleman kernel on $X \times X$ and if Int k is normal, then k^* is a bounded Carleman kernel.*

▶ Write $A = \text{Int } k$ and consider the polar decomposition $A = UP$, where P is positive and U is a partial isometry. Since $A^* = PU^*$ and $P = U^*A$, it follows that $A^* = U^*AU^*$. If A is normal, then A commutes with U and hence with U^* (by the Fuglede theorem), so that $A^* = A(U^*)^2$. Since Carleman operators form a right ideal (Theorem 11.6), it follows that A^* is a Carleman operator. ◀ [30]

70

Problem 11.12. Do all normal integral operators behave as well as normal Carleman operators? That is: *is the adjoint of every normal integral operator an integral operator?*

The adjoint of a bounded integral operator, even a Carleman operator, may fail to be an integral operator (Example 7.2); what can be said if the adjoint of a bounded Carleman operator does turn out to be an integral operator? Is the adjoint necessarily a Carleman operator? Equivalently: if a bounded Carleman kernel k is such that k^* is bounded, does it follow that k^* is a Carleman kernel? The answer is no.

Example 11.13. ▶ The Abel kernel k_0, defined on $\mathbb{I} \times \mathbb{I}$ by

$$k_0(x, y) = \begin{cases} 0 & \text{for } x \leq y, \\ \dfrac{1}{\sqrt{x - y}} & \text{for } x > y, \end{cases}$$

fails to be a Carleman kernel because of its behavior near the diagonal; if it is slightly modified there, it can even become square integrable.

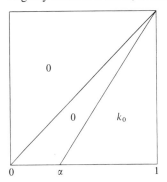

Consider, to be specific, a number α, $0 < \alpha < 1$, draw the line that joins $\langle \alpha, 0 \rangle$ to $\langle 1, 1 \rangle$, and define a kernel k_α to be equal to k_0 except between that line and the diagonal of the unit square, and there equal to 0. Note that since $0 \leq k_\alpha \leq k_0$, the kernel k_α is bounded and $\|k_\alpha\| \leq \|k_0\|$.

Elementary analytic geometry shows that the equation of the line is

$$x = y + \alpha(1 - y).$$

Elementary calculus shows that

$$\int_0^1 |k_\alpha(x, y)|^2\, dx = \int_{y + \alpha(1-y)}^1 \frac{dx}{x - y} = -\log \alpha.$$

Note that the latter happens to be a constant, independent of y; it follows that

$$\|k_\alpha\|_2^2 = \iint |k_\alpha(x, y)|^2\, dx\, dy = -\log \alpha < \infty.$$

Now let α take an infinite sequence of values, and place the corresponding kernels k_α, suitably weighted, side by side horizontally to form a kernel on $\mathbb{R}_+ \times \mathbb{I}$. Since the finiteness of vertical integrals is not affected by these steps, the result will still be a Carleman kernel; if, however, the α's and the weights are chosen right, the horizontal integrals can be made large enough to ruin the Carleman property of the adjoint.

To be precise, let k_n be the kernel k_α with $\alpha = e^{-n}$ (so that $-\log \alpha = n$), and define a kernel k on $\mathbb{R}_+ \times \mathbb{I}$ by writing

$$k(x, y) = \frac{1}{n} k_n(x - n + 1, y)$$

whenever $n - 1 \leqq x < n$, $n = 1, 2, 3, \dots$. Since

$$\sum_n \frac{1}{n^2} \|k_n\|^2 \leqq \sum_n \frac{1}{n^2} \|k_0\|^2 < \infty,$$

it follows that k is bounded. (Reason: whenever an operator A from a Hilbert space H to a direct sum of countably many copies of H is defined by

$$Af = \langle A_1 f, A_2 f, A_3 f, \dots \rangle,$$

where the A_n, of course, are operators on H, then

$$\|A\|^2 \leqq \sum_n \|A_n\|^2.)$$

Since $k(x, y) \geq 0$ for all $\langle x, y \rangle$, the kernel k is obviously absolutely bounded, and Corollary 10.6 implies that so is the (conjugate) transpose kernel. Since, however,

$$\int_0^\infty |k(x, y)|^2 \, dx = \sum_{n=1}^\infty \frac{1}{n^2} \cdot n = \sum_{n=1}^\infty \frac{1}{n} = \infty,$$

that transpose is not a Carleman kernel. ◄

§12. Compactness

Functions of one variable, when suitably compounded with the natural group operation of the line, yield a classically important class of kernels, the so-called *convolution kernels*. If, to be specific, φ is a measurable function on $\mathbb{R}$, the convolution kernel k_φ induced by φ is defined by

$$k_\varphi(x, y) = \varphi(x - y).$$

Most of the applications of convolution kernels are based on the following analytic statement about integrals.

Lemma 12.1. *If* $\varphi \in L^1(\mathbb{R})$ *and* $g \in L^1(\mathbb{R})$, *then* $k_\varphi(x, \cdot) g \in L^1(\mathbb{R})$ *for almost every* x. *If*

$$f(x) = \int k_\varphi(x, y) g(y) \, dy,$$

then $f \in L^1(\mathbb{R})$ *and*

$$\|f\|_1 \leq \|\varphi\|_1 \cdot \|g\|_1.$$

▶ The proof is a straightforward calculation:

$$
\begin{aligned}
\|f\|_1 &= \int |\int \varphi(x - y) g(y) \, dy| \, dx \\
&\leq \int\int |\varphi(x - y)| \cdot |g(y)| \, dy \, dx \\
&= \int |g(y)| (\int |\varphi(x - y)| \, dx) \, dy \\
&= \int |g(y)| (\int |\varphi(x)| \, dx) \, dy \\
&= \int |g(y)| \cdot \|\varphi\|_1 \, dy = \|\varphi\|_1 \cdot \|g\|_1. \quad ◀
\end{aligned}
$$

Lemma 12.1 says that convolution kernels induced by functions in L^1 induce bounded operators on L^1; the next result deduces from this that they induce bounded operators on L^2 as well.[31]

Theorem 12.2. *If* $\varphi \in L^1(\mathbb{R})$, *then the convolution kernel* k_φ *on* $\mathbb{R} \times \mathbb{R}$ *is (absolutely) bounded, and, in fact,*

$$\|k_\varphi\| \leq \|\varphi\|_1.$$

▶ Given a function g in $L^2(\mathbb{R})$, apply Lemma 12.1 to $|g|^2$ in place of g. It follows that

(1) $$\int\int |\varphi(x - y)| \cdot |g(y)|^2 \, dy \, dx \leq \|\varphi\|_1 \cdot \|g\|_2^2,$$

and hence that

$$|k_\varphi(x, \cdot)|^{1/2} \cdot |g| \in L^2(\mathbb{R})$$

for almost every x. The Schwarz inequality then yields

(2)
$$|\int \varphi(x-y)g(y)\,dy| \leq \int |\varphi(x-y)|^{1/2} \cdot |\varphi(x-y)|^{1/2}|g(y)|\,dy$$
$$\leq (\int |\varphi(x-y)|\,dy)^{1/2} (\int |\varphi(x-y)| \cdot |g(y)|^2\,dy)^{1/2}$$
$$= \|\varphi\|_1^{1/2} (\int |\varphi(x-y)| \cdot |g(y)|^2\,dy)^{1/2}.$$

Apply (1) to the last term of (2) and infer that

$$\int |\int \varphi(x-y)g(y)\,dy|^2\,dx \leq \|\varphi\|_1^2 \cdot \|g\|_2^2.$$

Absolute boundedness is immediate; the reasoning just used depends on $|\varphi|$ only. ◄

Corollary 12.3. *If* $\varphi \in L^1(-1, +1)$ *and if* $k_\varphi(x, y) = \varphi(x-y)$ *whenever* $\langle x, y \rangle \in \mathbb{I} \times \mathbb{I}$, *then* k_φ *is a bounded kernel on* $\mathbb{I} \times \mathbb{I}$ *and* $\mathrm{Int}\, k_\varphi$ *is compact.*

▶ To apply Theorem 12.2, extend φ to $\mathbb{R}$ by defining $\varphi(x)$ to be 0 whenever $|x| > 1$, and, correspondingly, extend k_φ to $\mathbb{R} \times \mathbb{R}$. The boundedness assertion of the corollary is then immediate: the k_φ of the corollary is a subkernel of the extended k_φ (cf. §9). It remains only to prove compactness.
    If φ happens to be in $L^2(-1, +1)$, then

$$\int_0^1 \int_0^1 |k_\varphi(x, y)|^2\,dx\,dy \leq \int_0^1 \int_{-1}^1 |\varphi(x-y)|^2\,dx\,dy$$
$$= \int_0^1 \int_{-1}^1 |\varphi(x)|^2\,dx\,dy = \|\varphi\|_2^2 < \infty,$$

so that $\mathrm{Int}\, k_\varphi$ is a Hilbert-Schmidt operator, and therefore compact (Corollary 4.8). In the general case, find a sequence $\{\varphi_n\}$ of elements of $L^2(-1, +1)$ that converges to φ in $L^1(-1, +1)$. If $k_n = k_{\varphi_n}$, then, by Theorem 12.2,

$$\|\mathrm{Int}\, k_\varphi - \mathrm{Int}\, k_n\| \leq \|\varphi - \varphi_n\|_1;$$

since each $\mathrm{Int}\, k_n$ is compact, it follows that $\mathrm{Int}\, k_\varphi$ is compact. ◄

These results make contact with Example 11.1. Indeed, if

$$\varphi_s(x) = \begin{cases} 0 & \text{for } -1 \leq x \leq 0, \\ \dfrac{1}{x^s} & \text{for } 0 < x \leq +1, \end{cases}$$

whenever $\frac{1}{2} \leq s < 1$, then the induced convolution kernels k_{φ_s} on $\mathbb{I} \times \mathbb{I}$ are exactly the kernels k_s defined in Example 11.1. If $\frac{1}{2} \leq s < 1$, then k_{φ_s} is not even a Carleman kernel – but, nevertheless, by Corollary 12.3, the integral operator it induces is compact.

Even though integral operators that are not compact are already available (Example 5.1), more and more evidence is piling up on the compact side. The Abel kernel is a relatively "large" one, in the sense that it is not square integrable, and not even semi-square-integrable, but its induced integral operator is compact just the same. The relation between integral operators and compactness deserves more study, and that is what this section and the next are about.

The compact Fourier transform (Example 7.2) is an isometry that is not an integral operator, and Theorem 8.6 says that over divisible spaces multiplication operators are not integral operators. All these operators are large in some sense. The most familiar integral operators in the classical literature, the Hilbert-Schmidt operators, are small in the sense that they are compact (Corollary 4.6). Is that the secret? Are all compact operators integral? The answer is no.

Example 12.4. ▶ In $L^2(\mathbb{I})$ there are orthonormal bases that are pointwise uniformly bounded (the often-used exponential basis is the most familiar example), and there are bases that consist of pointwise bounded functions whose essential supremum tends to ∞, and which, in fact, are arbitrarily large almost everywhere. (A sequence $\{h_n\}$ is arbitrarily large almost everywhere if $\sup_n |h_n(x)| = \infty$ almost everywhere.)

A good example of the second kind of basis is provided by the Haar functions

$$\{h_0^1; h_1^1, h_1^2; h_2^1, h_2^2, h_2^3, h_2^4; \ldots; h_n^1, \ldots, h_n^{2^n}; \ldots\}.$$

They are defined by $h_0^1 = 1$ and

$$h_n^j(x) = \begin{cases} \sqrt{2^n} & \text{if } x \in \left(\dfrac{j-1}{2^n}, \dfrac{j-\frac{1}{2}}{2^n}\right], \\ -\sqrt{2^n} & \text{if } x \in \left(\dfrac{j-\frac{1}{2}}{2^n}, \dfrac{j}{2^n}\right], \\ 0 & \text{otherwise,} \end{cases}$$

where $n = 0, 1, 2, 3, \ldots, j = 1, \ldots, 2^n$. The verification that they form an orthonormal basis is painless.[32]

Suppose now that $\{e_n\}$ is the exponential basis and $\{h_n\}$ is the Haar basis; for simplicity of notation rearrange both the e's and the h's in a simple sequence, so that they look like $\{e_0, e_1, e_2, \ldots\}$ and $\{h_0, h_1, h_2, \ldots\}$. Write $\lambda_n = 1/\sqrt{\|h_n\|_\infty}$. Since $\lambda_n \to 0$, the operator A defined by

$$A e_n = \lambda_n h_n$$

is compact.

(Caution: since $\|h_n^j\|_\infty = \sqrt{2^n}$, it is tempting to conclude that the sequence $\{\lambda_n\}$ is square summable and hence that A is a Hilbert-Schmidt operator. The conclusion is wrong. The trouble with the reasoning is that h_n has very little to do with h_n^j. The essential supremum of h_n^j is $\sqrt{2^n}$, for $j = 1, \ldots, 2^n$, and consequently the number $\sqrt{2^n}$ occurs 2^n times among the λ's.)

To prove that A is not an integral operator, digress for a moment and consider an arbitrary bounded · kernel k on $\mathbb{I} \times \mathbb{I}$. Since $1 \in L^2(\mathbb{I})$, it follows that

$$\Omega(x) = \int |k(x, y)| \, dy < \infty$$

for almost every x. The function Ω (measurable, finite, positive) has the property that if $g \in L^\infty(\mathbb{I})$, then

$$|(\text{Int } k) g(x)| \leq \|g\|_\infty \cdot \Omega(x)$$

almost everywhere. In other words: in order for an operator A to be integral, it is necessary that there exist such a function Ω with the property that if $g \in L^\infty(\mathbb{I})$, then

$$|A g(x)| \leq \|g\|_\infty \cdot \Omega(x).$$

Assertion: the particular compact operator A defined above does not satisfy this necessary condition.

Indeed: if there were such a function, then it would follow that

$$|A e_n(x)| \leq \Omega(x)$$

almost everywhere. Since, however,

$$|A e_n(x)| = |\lambda_n h_n(x)|,$$

and since $\{|\lambda_n h_n|\}$ is arbitrarily large almost everywhere, this implies that $\Omega(x) = \infty$ almost everywhere, which is a contradiction.

Is there a compact *Hermitian* operator on $L^2(\mathbb{I})$ that is not integral? There is an easy but unsatisfactory way to answer the question. Consider the real and imaginary parts of the operator A just constructed. Both are compact, but not both can be integral, for then A would be. Hence: yes, a compact Hermitian operator that is not integral exists, but this proof is not sharp enough to name one.

An explicit construction based on the same A is available: form L^2 of the direct sum $\mathbb{I} \oplus \mathbb{I}$, and consider on it the operator defined by the matrix $\begin{pmatrix} 0 & A^* \\ A & 0 \end{pmatrix}$. It is compact, obviously, and Hermitian. It maps vectors in the first direct summand into the second one, but, except for that, its action is exactly the same as that of A, and, therefore, it cannot be an integral operator any more than A can.

One final comment: the *non*-existence of kernels is usually easy to extend from the finite to the infinite case without the use of the isomorphism theorem (6.2). Thus, for instance, Theorem 6.2 is not needed to infer from the present example that there exists a compact operator on $L^2(\mathbb{R}_+)$ that is not integral. The inference is simpler as follows. Regard $L^2(\mathbb{R}_+)$ as the direct sum $L^2(\mathbb{I}) \oplus L^2(1, \infty)$, and define a compact operator on $L^2(\mathbb{R}_+)$ as the corresponding direct sum of the one just described and 0. If the result were an integral operator, with kernel k, then the restriction of k to $\mathbb{I} \times \mathbb{I}$ would be a kernel that induces the operator just described. ◀ [33]

§13. $\langle 2, 1 \rangle$ Compactness

Integral operators need not be compact, and compact operators need not be integral. These are negative statements; can anything positive be said? Yes, there is something positive and useful that can be said, at the cost, to be sure, of some loss of generality, but the gain is well worth the price.

The loss of generality is in the assumption, to be made in most of the remainder of this section, that the measures in the underlying spaces are not only sigma-finite, but actually finite. (Once that assumption is made, then the measures might as well be normalized so that $\mu(X) = v(Y) = 1$, and that normalization assumption is hereby put in force.) It follows from the finiteness of the measure in X that associated with every bounded operator A from $L^2(Y)$ to $L^2(X)$ there is a bounded operator from $L^2(Y)$ to $L^1(X)$, namely A itself. More clearly said: since (by the Schwarz inequality) $L^2(X) \subset L^1(X)$, it follows that if $g \in L^2(Y)$, then

$$\|A g\|_1 \leq \|A g\|_2 \leq \|A\| \cdot \|g\|_2,$$

so that if

$$A_{2,1}: \; L^2(Y) \to L^1(X)$$

is defined by $A_{2,1} g = A g$, then

$$\|A_{2,1}\| \leq \|A\|.$$

So far no assumption was needed about the finiteness of the measure in Y. The main purpose of what follows is to show that if the measure in Y also is finite, then, for every bounded integral operator A from $L^2(Y)$ to $L^2(X)$, the corresponding operator $A_{2,1}$ is compact.

The easy way for $A_{2,1}$ to be compact is for A itself to be compact. Indeed: $A_{2,1}$ is the product (composition) of A (from L^2 to L^2) and the injection mapping (from L^2 to L^1); since the first factor is compact, so is the product. Consequence: if $A_{2,1}$ is the limit (in the topology induced by the $\langle 2, 1 \rangle$ norm) of a sequence of operators that are compact (in the ordinary sense), then it is the limit of a sequence of operators that are $\langle 2, 1 \rangle$ compact, and, consequently, it itself is $\langle 2, 1 \rangle$ compact. (The "$\langle 2, 1 \rangle$ norm" of A is, of course, $\|A_{2,1}\|$; to say that A is "$\langle 2, 1 \rangle$ compact" means that $A_{2,1}$ is compact.)

The reason that integral operators turn out to be compact in some sense is that they are *absolutely continuous* in some sense. To define what that means, recall that for each measurable subset G of a measure space Y the characteristic function χ_G induces a multiplication operator $Q_G(Q_G g(y) = \chi_G(y) g(y))$. If A is an operator from $L^2(Y)$ to $L^2(X)$, then so is AQ_G. The pertinent sense of absolute continuity is that

$$\|A_{2,1} Q_G\| (= \|(AQ_G)_{2,1}\|) \to 0$$

as $v(G) \to 0$.

There are two precise ways to formulate this requirement: the epsilontic and the sequential. One is that for every $\varepsilon > 0$ there exists a $\delta > 0$ such that if $v(G) < \delta$, then $\|A_{2,1} Q_G\| < \varepsilon$; the other is that if $\{G_n\}$ is a decreasing sequence of sets with $v(G_n) \to 0$, then $\|A_{2,1} Q_{G_n}\| \to 0$. It is an easy analytic exercise to prove that the two formulations are equivalent. For $A_{2,1}$ to make sense, the underlying measure μ in X must be finite, of course; for much of the theory it is either necessary or convenient to assume that the measure v in Y is finite also.

What follows now is (1) a technical measure-theoretic lemma, easy enough, of some possible independent interest, and of use in proving the absolute continuity that is needed, (2) a proof of absolute continuity, and then (3) a proof of the compactness assertion. The latter is broken up into several steps and is accompanied by some pertinent discussion that may be helpful for understanding but is not indispensable for the proof.

Lemma 13.1. *If $\mu(X) < \infty$, if $\{F_n\}$ is a sequence of subsets of X with $\mu(F_n) \geq \delta > 0$ for all n, and if $\{\alpha_n\}$ is a sequence of scalars such that $\sum_n |\alpha_n| \chi_{F_n}(x) < \infty$ for almost every x, then $\sum_n |\alpha_n| < \infty$.*

▶ Write $f(x) = \sum_n |\alpha_n| \chi_{F_n}(x)$. If $E_m = \{x : f(x) > m\}$, then $\mu(E_m) \to 0$ as $m \to \infty$, and, consequently, $\mu(F_n \cap E_m) < \delta/2$ as soon as m is large enough. Choose m_0 that large, note that $\mu(F_n - E_{m_0}) \geq \delta/2$, and note that $\sum_n |\alpha_n| \chi_{F_n}(x) \leq m_0$ whenever $x \in X - E_{m_0}$. These observations justify the assumption that $\sum_n |\alpha_n| \chi_{F_n}(x) \leq m_0$ for almost every x—just replace X by $X - E_{m_0}$, F_n by $F_n - E_{m_0}$, and δ by $\delta/2$. The monotone convergence theorem then implies that $\sum_n |\alpha_n| \mu(F_n) \leq m_0 \mu(X)$; since $\mu(F_n) \geq \delta$ for all n, the conclusion follows. ◀

Lemma 13.2. *If k is a bounded kernel on $X \times Y$, where the measures μ and v in X and Y are finite, if $\{G_n\}$ is a decreasing sequence of measurable subsets of Y with $v(G_n) \to 0$, if $A = \text{Int}\, k$, and if Q_n is the multiplication operator on $L^2(Y)$ induced by χ_{G_n}, then $\|A_{2,1} Q_n\| \to 0$.*

▶ Proceed by contradiction: if the conclusion is false, then some subsequence of $\{\|A_{2,1} Q_n\|\}$ is bounded away from 0. Assume (with no loss) that the whole sequence has this property, so that, for some ε,

$$\|A_{2,1} Q_n\| > \varepsilon > 0$$

for all n.

Assertion (∗): there exist unit vectors g_n in $L^2(Y)$ and positive integers j_n increasing to ∞ such that

(a) support $g_n \subset Y - G_{j_n}$,

(b) support $g_n \cap$ support $g_m = \varnothing$ when $n \neq m$,

(c) $\|Ag_n\|_1 > \varepsilon$ for all n.

The proof of assertion (∗) can be achieved by induction. To set the machine in motion, let h be a unit vector in $L^2(Y)$ such that $\|AQ_1h\|_1 > \varepsilon$. Since $Q_n g \to 0$ for each g, it follows that

$$A(1 - Q_n)Q_1 h \to AQ_1 h$$

in $L^2(X)$ and hence in $L^1(X)$. This implies that

$$\lim_n \|A(1 - Q_n)Q_1 h\|_1 > \varepsilon$$

and hence that

$$\|A(1 - Q_{j_1})Q_1 h\| > \varepsilon$$

for some j_1. Normalize the vector so obtained; that is, put

$$g_1 = \frac{(1 - Q_{j_1})Q_1 h}{\|(1 - Q_{j_1})Q_1 h\|_2}.$$

The result is a unit vector g_1 in $L^2(Y)$ such that

$$\text{support } g_1 \subset G_1 - G_{j_1} \subset Y - G_{j_1}$$

and

$$\|Ag_1\|_1 > \frac{\varepsilon}{\|(1 - Q_{j_1})Q_1 h\|_2} \geq \varepsilon.$$

Assume now that $g_1, \ldots, g_p$ and $j_1, \ldots, j_p$ have been found satisfying (a), (b), (c) when $n, m \leq p$. If N is a positive integer such that $j_p < N$, then

$$\text{support } g_n \subset Y - G_N$$

for $n = 1, \ldots, p$. Repeat the argument of the preceding paragraph as follows: let h be a unit vector in $L^2(Y)$ such that

$$\|AQ_N h\|_1 > \varepsilon,$$

find $j_{p+1} > N$ so that

$$\|A(1 - Q_{j_{p+1}})Q_N h\|_1 > \varepsilon,$$

and put

$$g_{p+1} = \frac{(1 - Q_{j_{p+1}})Q_n h}{\|(1 - Q_{j_{p+1}})Q_n h\|_2}.$$

This completes the proof of (∗).

If $F_n = \left\{ x : |A g_n(x)| \geq \dfrac{\varepsilon}{2} \right\}$, then

$$\varepsilon < \|A g_n\|_1 = \int |A g_n(x)| \, dx$$

$$= (\chi_{F_n}, |A g_n|) + \int_{X - F_n} |A g_n(x)| \, dx$$

$$\leq \|\chi_{F_n}\|_2 \cdot \|A g_n\|_2 + \frac{\varepsilon}{2} \mu(X - F_n)$$

$$\leq \|\chi_{F_n}\|_2 \cdot \|A\| + \frac{\varepsilon}{2},$$

and therefore

$$\frac{\varepsilon}{2 \|A\|} < \|\chi_{F_n}\|_2 = \sqrt{\mu(F_n)}.$$

Since the g_n's constitute an orthonormal sequence, it follows that

$$g = \sum_{n=1}^{\infty} \frac{1}{n} g_n \in L^2 ;$$

note that, since the supports of the g_n's are disjoint,

$$|g| = \sum_{n=1}^{\infty} \frac{1}{n} |g_n|.$$

Since k is a bounded kernel, therefore

$$\int |k(x, y)| \cdot |g(y)| \, dy < \infty$$

for almost every x. Apply A to $|g|$ and infer that

$$\sum_{n=1}^{\infty} \frac{1}{n} \int |k(x, y)| \cdot |g_n(y)| \, dy < \infty$$

for almost every x, and hence that

$$\sum_{n=1}^{\infty} \frac{1}{n} |A g_n(x)| < \infty$$

almost everywhere. The definition of the F_n's implies that

$$\frac{\varepsilon}{2} \chi_{F_n}(x) \leq |A g_n(x)|$$

almost everywhere, and therefore

$$\sum_{n=1}^{\infty} \frac{1}{n} \chi_{F_n}(x) < \infty$$

almost everywhere. In view of Lemma 13.1 this is a contradiction, and the proof is complete. ◄

Does the absolute continuity conclusion of Lemma 13.2 apply to every bounded operator? The answer is no: there exists an operator A on $L^2(\mathbb{I})$ that is not absolutely continuous in the $\langle 2, 1 \rangle$ sense.

Example 13.3. The idea is that for characteristic functions the L^2 norm is much larger than the L^1 norm, whereas for functions with constant modulus the two norms are the same. It follows that if (after an appropriate adjustment of scale factors) many characteristic functions are mapped onto functions of constant modulus, then the L^2 norm can be kept under control at the same time as the L^1 norm gets large.

▶ Let G_n be the interval $(1/2^n, 1/2^{n-1})$, let χ_n be its characteristic function, and write $u_n = \sqrt{2^n}\, \chi_n$. Since

$$\|u_n\|_2 = \sqrt{2^n}\, \|\chi_n\|_2 = \sqrt{2^n}\,\sqrt{\mu(G_n)} = 1,$$

it follows that the functions u_n form an orthonormal set. Let $\{e_n : n = 0, \pm 1, \pm 2, \ldots\}$ be the usual exponential basis (consisting of functions of constant modulus 1). It is easy to see (complete the u's to an orthonormal basis and map the new elements of that basis onto the e's with negative index) that there exists a bounded operator A (in fact a unitary one) such that $A u_n = e_n$, $n = 1, 2, 3, \ldots$.

Assertion: $A_{2,1}$ is not absolutely continuous. In fact, there exist sets G of arbitrarily small measure such that $\|A_{2,1} Q_G\| = 1$. Indeed: if $G = G_n$, then

$$\|A_{2,1} Q_G u_n\| = \|A_{2,1}(\chi_n u_n)\|_1 = \|A u_n\|_1 = \|e_n\|_1 = 1,$$

which implies that $\|A_{2,1} Q_G\| \geq 1$. The reverse inequality is trivial, since A is unitary. ◄

The best known compactness theorem in the theory of integral operators concerns Hilbert-Schmidt operators: if k is square integrable, then $\mathrm{Int}\, k$ is compact. The following result weakens the assumption and correspondingly weakens the conclusion, but it is of the same type: it says that if something is square integrable, then something is compact.

Lemma 13.4. *If k is a bounded kernel on $X \times Y$, where the measures μ and ν in X and Y are finite, such that*

$$\int (\int |k(x, y)|\, dx)^2\, dy < \infty,$$

and if $A = \mathrm{Int}\, k$, then $A_{2,1}$ is compact.

▶ The main tool in the proof is the relation

$$\|A_{2,1}\|^2 \leq \int (\int |k(x, y)|\, dx)^2\, dy.$$

To prove it, take g in $L^2(X)$ and compute:

$$\|A_{2,1}g\|_1^2=(\int|\int k(x,y)\,g(y)\,dy|\,dx)^2$$
$$\leq(\iint|k(x,y)|\cdot|g(y)|\cdot dx\,dy)^2$$
$$=(\int(\int|k(x,y)|\,dx)\cdot|g(y)|\,dy)^2$$
$$\leq\int(\int|k(x,y)|\,dx)^2\,dy\cdot\|g\|_2^2.$$

Since

$$\iint|k(x,y)|\,dx\,dy\leq(\int(\int|k(x,y)|\,dx)^2\,dy)^{1/2},$$

the assumption implies that $|k|$ is finite almost everywhere, and hence that the sets

$$E_n=\{\langle x,y\rangle:|k(x,y)|\leq n\}$$

increase to $X\times Y$ as $n\to\infty$. If

$$k_n(x,y)=\chi_{E_n}(x,y)\,k(x,y),$$

then $|k_n|\leq n$ and $k_n(x,y)\to k(x,y)$ for every $\langle x,y\rangle$. Since k_n is square integrable, the kernel k_n is bounded; if $A_n=\mathrm{Int}\,k_n$, then A_n is a Hilbert-Schmidt operator, and therefore compact.

The proof of the lemma can be completed by showing that

$$\|A_{2,1}-(A_n)_{2,1}\|\to0$$

as $n\to\infty$. Since

$$\|A_{2,1}-(A_n)_{2,1}\|^2\leq\int(\int|k(x,y)-k_n(x,y)|\,dx)^2\,dy$$
$$=\iiint|k(x,y)-k_n(x,y)|\cdot|k(z,y)-k_n(z,y)|\,dx\,dz\,dy,$$

the problem is to prove that the integral on the right tends to 0. The integrand obviously does tend pointwise to 0, and since $|k-k_n|\leq|k|$, the integrand is dominated by

$$|k(x,y)|\cdot|k(z,y)|.$$

Since, finally,

$$\iiint|k(x,y)|\cdot|k(z,y)|\,dx\,dz\,dy=\int(\int|k(x,y)|\,dx)^2\,dy<\infty,$$

so that the dominant is integrable, the Lebesgue dominated convergence theorem yields the desired conclusion. ◀

Example 13.5. How much of a restriction is the assumption of Lemma 13.4. Could it be that for finite measures the assumption is always satisfied? The answer had better be no—and it is.

▶ An example is conveniently given in terms of matrices. The inflate-and-change-measure technique (see §9) converts a matrix a into the kernel k on $\mathbb{I}\times\mathbb{I}$

82

defined by

$$k(x, y) = \frac{a(m, n)}{(1-x)(1-y)}$$

when

$$\langle x, y \rangle \in \left(1 - \frac{1}{m}, 1 - \frac{1}{m+1}\right) \times \left(1 - \frac{1}{n}, 1 - \frac{1}{n+1}\right),$$

$n = 1, 2, 3, \ldots$. For such a kernel

$$\int |k(x, y)| \, dx = \frac{1}{1-y} \sum_{m=1}^{\infty} |a(m, n)| \log\left(1 + \frac{1}{m}\right)$$

when $y \in \left(1 - \frac{1}{n}, 1 - \frac{1}{n+1}\right)$, and therefore

$$\int (\int |k(x, y)| \, dx)^2 \, dy = \sum_{n=1}^{\infty} \left(\sum_{m=1}^{\infty} |a(m, n)| \log\left(1 + \frac{1}{m}\right)\right)^2.$$

All that is needed therefore is a bounded matrix a for which the last expression is infinite.

One way to construct such a matrix is as an infinite direct sum of finite matrices. A typical direct summand can be a unitary matrix of size p, say, all whose entries have absolute value $1/\sqrt{p}$ (cf. Example 10.3). Let p run over a sequence of integers $p_1, p_2, \ldots$ such that the sums of the blocks of the (divergent) series $\sum_m \log\left(1 + \frac{1}{m}\right)$ between $s_j = p_1 + \cdots + p_j$ and $s_{j+1} = p_1 + \cdots + p_j + p_{j+1}$ are bounded from below, by ε say. Consequence (after a small computation): the direct sum matrix a so obtained is such that

$$\sum_n \left(\sum_m |a(m, n)| \log\left(1 + \frac{1}{m}\right)\right)^2 = \sum_{j=1}^{\infty} p_j \left(\frac{1}{\sqrt{p_j}} \sum_{m=s_j+1}^{s_{j+1}} \log\left(1 + \frac{1}{m}\right)\right)^2$$

$$\geq \sum_{j=1}^{\infty} \varepsilon^2 = \infty. \quad \blacktriangleleft$$

Remark 13.6. ▶ The relation between the kernels that occur in Lemma 13.4, the ones for which

$$\int (\int |k(x, y)| \, dx)^2 \, dy < \infty,$$

and the square integrable kernels that induce the Hilbert-Schmidt operators is deeper than just the occurrence of the exponent 2 in their definitions. The real relation is that square integrability is a special case of a general condition on L^p norms.

Suppose, indeed, that $1 \leq p \leq \infty$, and $1 \leq q \leq \infty$; write q' for the conjugate exponent defined by $\frac{1}{q} + \frac{1}{q'} = 1$. The safe way to guarantee that a kernel k will induce a bounded transformation from $L^q(Y)$ to $L^p(X)$ (in the sense in which a square integrable kernel safely yields a bounded transformation from $L^2(Y)$ to $L^2(X)$) is to assume that

$$k(x, \cdot) \in L^{q'}(Y)$$

for almost every x and that the function h defined by

$$h(x) = \|k(x, \cdot)\|_{q'}$$

belongs to $L^p(X)$. The point is that the q' condition on k guarantees that $k(x, \cdot) g \in L^1(Y)$ almost everywhere for each g in $L^q(Y)$, and the p condition on h guarantees that the transform of g belongs to $L^p(X)$. The details of the proof are a straightforward $\langle p, q \rangle$ modification of the Hilbert-Schmidt result. The operators induced by kernels satisfying the assumptions described are called the *Hille-Tamarkin operators* of class $\langle p, q \rangle$.[34]

Hille-Tamarkin operators are not only bounded, they are even compact. The compactness conclusion of Lemma 13.4 is an instance of that fact. Indeed, the assumption of Lemma 13.4 is that the (conjugate) transpose kernel k^* satisfies the Hille-Tamarkin condition $\langle 2, \infty \rangle$, and, consequently, it induces a compact operator from $L^\infty(Y)$ to $L^2(Y)$. It is possible to infer (via known facts about duality) that k itself induces a compact operator from $L^2(Y)$ to $L^1(X)$—and that's exactly what Lemma 13.4 says. (The principal "known fact about duality" needed is Schauder's theorem, the one that says that an operator is compact if and only if its adjoint is compact.) The proof of Lemma 13.4 given above is, of course, a direct proof of just a small part of the Hille-Tamarkin theory.

Results such as the compactness of Hille-Tamarkin operators, and, deeper and more important, such as the $\langle p, q \rangle$ compactness of integral operators for various values of p and q under conditions less stringent than the Hille-Tamarkin ones, have played an important role for some time. The case $p = 2$, $q = 1$ is the most delicate and the newest. ◀[35]

Lemma 13.7. *If k is a bounded kernel on $X \times Y$, where the measures μ and ν in X and Y are finite, such that $k \in L^1(X \times Y)$, and if $A = \operatorname{Int} k$, then $A_{2,1}$ is compact.*

▶ If $G_n = \{y : \int |k(x, y)| \, dx > n\}$, $n = 1, 2, 3, \ldots$, then $\{G_n\}$ is a decreasing sequence of sets with $\nu(G_n) \to 0$. If, as before, Q_n is the multiplication operator induced on $L^2(Y)$ by χ_{G_n}, then $A(1 - Q_n)$ is an integral operator, with kernel k_n defined by

$$k_n(x, y) = k(x, y)(1 - \chi_{G_n}(y)).$$

Since

$$\int \left(\int |k_n(x, y)| \, dx \right)^2 dy = \int (1 - \chi_{G_n}(y))^2 \left(\int |k(x, y)| \, dx \right)^2 dy$$
$$\leq n^2 \, \nu(Y) < \infty,$$

Lemma 13.4 implies that $(A(1 - Q_n))_{2,1}$ is compact. Since

$$\|A_{2,1} - (A(1 - Q_n))_{2,1}\| = \|A_{2,1} Q_n\|,$$

the asserted conclusion follows from Lemma 13.3. ◀

Theorem 13.8. *If k is a bounded kernel on $X \times Y$, where the measures μ and v in X and Y are finite, and if $A = \text{Int } k$, then $A_{2,1}$ is compact.*

▶ Since $1 \in L^2(Y)$, the boundedness of k implies that

$$\int |k(x,y)| \, dy < \infty$$

for almost every x. If

$$F_n = \{x : \int |k(x,y)| \, dy > n\},$$

$n = 1, 2, 3, \ldots$, then $\{F_n\}$ is a decreasing sequence of sets with $\mu(F_n) \to 0$. If P_n is the multiplication operator induced on $L^2(X)$ by χ_{F_n}, then $(1 - P_n)A$ is an integral operator, with kernel k_n defined by

$$k_n(x,y) = (1 - \chi_{F_n}(x)) \, k(x,y).$$

Since

$$\iint |k_n(x,y)| \, dx \, dy = \int (1 - \chi_{F_n}(x))(\int |k(x,y)| \, dy) \, dx$$
$$\leq n \mu(X) < \infty,$$

Lemma 13.7 implies that $((1 - P_n)A)_{2,1}$ is compact. Since

$$\|A_{2,1} - ((1 - P_n)A)_{2,1}\| = \|(P_n A)_{2,1}\| \leq \|(P_n)_{2,1}\| \cdot \|A\|,$$

the desired conclusion can be inferred as soon as it is known that $\|(P_n)_{2,1}\| \to 0$ − and that is easy to prove. Indeed: if $f \in L^2(X)$, then

$$\|P_n f\|_1 = \int \chi_{F_n}(x) \, |f(x)| \, dx = (\chi_{F_n}, |f|)$$
$$\leq \|\chi_{F_n}\| \cdot \|f\| = \sqrt{\mu(F_n)} \cdot \|f\|,$$

which implies that

$$\|(P_n)_{2,1}\| \leq \sqrt{\mu(F_n)}. \quad \blacktriangleleft^{36}$$

Corollary 13.9. *If k is a bounded kernel on $X \times Y$, where the measures μ and v in X and Y are finite, then there exists a sequence $\{k_n\}$ of square integrable kernels such that*

$$\|(\text{Int } k - \text{Int } k_n)_{2,1}\| \to 0;$$

in other words, Hilbert-Schmidt operators, over finite measure spaces, are $\langle 2, 1 \rangle$ dense in the set of all integral operators.

▶ The assertion is not really a corollary of the preceding results in the sense that it is an immediate consequence (or a special case) of their statements; it is, rather, an immediate consequence of their proofs. Indeed: the proof of Lemma 13.4 $\langle 2, 1 \rangle$ approximates the given kernel with pointwise bounded kernels; the proof of Lemma 13.7 $\langle 2, 1 \rangle$ approximates integrable kernels with the kind to which Lemma 13.4 applies; and the proof of Theorem 13.8 $\langle 2, 1 \rangle$ approximates arbitrary bounded kernels with integrable ones. ◀

§14. Essential Spectrum

Some operators are not induced by kernels and others that seem to resemble them a great deal are so induced. For pertinent examples, recall the identity operator on $L^2(\mathbb{R}_+)$ (which is not an integral operator) and the tensor product of the identity operator on $L^2(\mathbb{Z}_+)$ with a projection of rank 1 on $L^2(\mathbb{I})$ (which is an integral operator). What is the essential difference between these two kinds of examples?

The answer has to do with invertibility, and an interestingly circuitous route to the answer is via tensor products and their spectra.

In set theory, Cartesian multiplication is distributive over union; if X, Y, and Z are sets, then

$$X \times (Y \cup Z) = (X \times Y) \cup (X \times Z).$$

It follows that for L^2 spaces tensor multiplication is distributive over direct sum:

$$f \otimes (g \oplus h) = (f \otimes g) \oplus (f \otimes h).$$

If, that is, X, Y, and Z are measure spaces, with Y and Z disjoint, and if f, g, and h are elements of L^2 over X, Y, and Z respectively, then

$$f \otimes (g \oplus h) \in L^2(X \times (Y \cup Z))$$

and

$$(f \otimes g) \oplus (f \otimes h) \in L^2(X \times Y) \oplus L^2(X \times Z),$$

and the meanings of the symbols imply the asserted equation. (Note: symbols such as $g \oplus h$ have only one possible meaning, namely, the function on the disjoint union $Y \oplus Z$ whose value at y, in Y, is $g(y)$, and whose value at z, in Z, is $h(z)$.)

The preceding equations from set theory and linear algebra imply a corresponding equation from operator theory: tensor multiplication of operators (on L^2 spaces, or, for that matter, on abstract Hilbert spaces) is distributive over direct sum. Explicitly:

$$A \otimes (B \oplus C) = (A \otimes B) \oplus (A \otimes C).$$

For the proof it is sufficient to verify that the two sides of the equation have the same effect on vectors of the form

$$f \otimes (g \oplus h) (= (f \otimes g) \oplus (f \otimes h)),$$

and that is obvious from the definitions of direct sum and tensor product for operators and from the algebraic distributive law discussed above.

The facts about the spectra of direct sums and tensor products of operators are known. The results are these: the spectrum of $A \oplus B$ is the union of the spectra of A and B, and the spectrum of $A \otimes B$ is the product of the spectra of A and B, where the product of sets means the set of all products of the form $\alpha\beta$ with α and β in the spectrum of A and B respectively. The proof for direct sums is an elementary exercise; the proof for tensor products is harder. In at least one important special case the proof for tensor products is transparent, namely when one of the factors is a projection.[37]

Example 14.1. ▶ Since $A \otimes 1$ is the direct sum of copies of A (equal in number to the dimension of the domain of the identity factor 1), it follows that the spectrum of $A \otimes 1$ is equal to the spectrum of A; the only possible difference between the spectral properties of A and $A \otimes 1$ is an undefined but intuitively plausible concept of multiplicity. Since $A \otimes 0 = 0$, it follows that the spectrum of $A \otimes 0$ consists of 0 alone. These two special cases are evidence for the general multiplicative formula, but, more than that, between them they are almost a complete proof of that formula as far as it applies to projections. Indeed, if P is a projection, then $P = 1 \oplus 0$ in an obvious sense, and therefore $A \otimes P = (A \otimes 1) \oplus (A \otimes 0)$. In other words, $A \otimes P$ is the direct sum of two operators, one of which is a direct sum of copies of A and the other is 0; the sizes of the two operators are determined by the sizes of the direct summands 1 and 0 in P. Conclusion: the spectrum of $A \otimes P$ is equal to the union of the spectrum of A (with "multiplicity" equal to the rank of P) and the singleton 0 (with multiplicity equal to the nullity of P). ◀

The preceding example calls attention to the main difference between the inflation of the identity matrix and the identity operator on, say, $L^2(\mathbb{R}_+)$. More generally, if k is an arbitrary matrix and if k' is the kernel on $\mathbb{I} \times \mathbb{I}$ defined by $k'(x', y') = 1$ for all $\langle x', y' \rangle$, then $\operatorname{Int} k$ and $\operatorname{Int}(k \otimes k')$ have essentially the same spectrum except for 0; the trouble with 0 is that even if the former is invertible, the latter always has an infinite-dimensional null-space. (Here is one of the few places in mathematics where the use of "kernel" for "null-space" might lead to confusion.) From the point of view of tensor products of operators, $\operatorname{Int}(k \otimes k') = \operatorname{Int} k \otimes \operatorname{Int} k'$, this observation becomes algebraically obvious.[38]

All this is a step toward understanding that some operators are more invertible than others. What, for instance, are the invertibility differences between the identity operator 1, a projection P_1 whose range is a subspace of finite (but non-zero) codimension, and a projection P_∞ whose range is a subspace of infinite codimension? The identity operator is invertible and the other two are not, but more than that can be said, namely that P_1 is essentially invertible, but P_∞ is not. Definition: *an operator A is essentially right (or left) invertible if there exists an operator B such that $1 - AB$ (or $1 - BA$) is compact; A is essentially invertible if there exists an operator B such that both $1 - AB$ and $1 - BA$ are compact.* (If A is both essentially right and left invertible, then it is essentially invertible, and, in fact, the difference between the essential right and left inverses is compact, and either one serves as an essential inverse. Reason: if $1 - AB_1 = C_1$ and $1 - B_2 A = C_2$, then

$$(1 - C_2)B_1 = B_2 A B_1 = B_2(1 - C_1),$$

so that

$$B_1 = B_2 + C,$$

where $C = C_2 B_1 - B_2 C_1$, and therefore

$$B_1 A = B_2 A + CA = 1 - C_2 + CA.)$$

The use of "essential" in this sense has gained wide acceptance; in operator theory the word is now reserved almost exclusively to indicate concepts modulo the ideal of compact operators. The operator P_∞ is not essentially invertible: $\ker BP_\infty$ is always infinite-dimensional, so that $1 - BP_\infty$ is always equal to the identity operator on an infinite-dimensional subspace, and, consequently, $1 - BP_\infty$ can never be compact.

The theory of essential invertibility is greatly simplified by the following remarkable result, called *Atkinson's theorem*, which says, in effect, that from the "essential" point of view it does not matter whether the ideal used consists of all compact operators or of the operators of finite rank only.

Theorem 14.2. *If an operator A has an essential left inverse, then there exists an operator B_0 such that $1 - B_0 A$ has finite rank. In fact $\ker A$ is finite-dimensional, and B_0 can be chosen so that $B_0 A f = f$ whenever $f \in \ker^\perp A$. Similar assertions are true for right inverses.*[39]

▶ Suppose first that A is essentially left invertible, so that for some operator B the difference $C = 1 - BA$ is compact. Assertion: BA is bounded from below on $\ker^\perp BA$. If not, then there exist unit vectors f_n in $\ker^\perp BA$ such that $BAf_n \to 0$. The compactness of C justifies the assumption that the sequence $\{Cf_n\}$ converges, to f say (because some subsequence does converge). It follows that $f_n = Cf_n + BAf_n \to f$, so that $f \in \ker^\perp BA$ and $\|f\| = 1$. But if $f_n \to f$, then $BAf_n \to BAf$, so that $BAf = 0$; this says that $f \in \ker BA$, so that $f = 0$, and that is a contradiction.

Not only BA but also A is bounded from below on $\ker^\perp BA$. Reason: $\|BAf\| \leq \|B\| \cdot \|Af\|$. Consequence: the image under A of $\ker^\perp BA$ is closed.

Since $BA = 1 - C$, and since the multiplicity of 1 as an eigenvalue of C must be finite, it follows that the dimension of $\ker BA$ is finite. This implies that the image under A of $\ker BA$ is finite-dimensional also, and hence that $\operatorname{ran} A$ ($= A(\ker BA) + A(\ker^\perp BA)$) is closed.

Since the restriction of A to $\ker^\perp A$ is a one-to-one mapping onto $\operatorname{ran} A$, the closed graph theorem implies that that restriction has a bounded inverse. Let B_0 be the operator that is equal to that inverse on $\operatorname{ran} A$ and is equal to 0 on $\operatorname{ran}^\perp A$. Since $B_0 A = 0$ on $\ker A$ and $B_0 A = 1$ on $\ker^\perp A$, the product $B_0 A$ is the projection with range $\ker^\perp A$; since $\ker A$ ($\subset \ker BA$) is finite-dimensional, it follows that $1 - B_0 A$ is of finite rank.

The proof for *left* invertibility is complete. For *right* invertibility, apply the left result to A^*. (If $1 - AB$ is compact, then $1 - B^* A^*$ is compact; find B_0 so that $1 - B_0 A^*$ has finite rank, and conclude that $1 - AB_0^*$ has finite rank.) ◄

For operators on ℓ^2 induced by diagonal matrices the degrees of invertibility can be read off from the sequence of diagonal entries. Such an operator is essentially invertible exactly when 0 is not a limit point of the diagonal; it is invertible exactly when 0 is neither a term nor a limit point of the diagonal, i.e., when 0 is not in the closure of the diagonal.

"Closure" may be a misleading word here. The diagonal is a sequence, i.e., a function on $\mathbb{Z}_+$, which is not the same as the set of its terms, i.e., the range of the function. An equivalent way of describing essential invertibility for operators induced by diagonal matrices is this: the operator is *not* essentially invertible exactly when 0 is either an eigenvalue of infinite multiplicity or a cluster point of eigenvalues. This formulation generalizes to arbitrary normal operators on arbitrary Hilbert spaces: a normal operator is *not* essentially invertible exactly when 0 is either an eigenvalue of infinite multiplicity or a cluster point of the spectrum. The statement can be rephrased so as to yield another satisfactory and usable characterization of essential invertibility for normal operators, one that is pleasantly reminiscent of the definition of the essential range of a measurable function.

Theorem 14.3. *A necessary and sufficient condition that a normal operator A with spectral measure E be essentially (either right or left) invertible is that there exist a neighborhood N of 0 in the complex plane such that* $\operatorname{rank} E(N) < \infty$.

▶ Suppose that there is such a neighborhood N. The range of $E(N)$ reduces A, and the restriction of A to the orthogonal complement of that range is invertible (because it is normal and bounded from below). Subtract the operator $E(N)AE(N)$ (of finite rank) from A, and add the operator $E(N)$; the result is an invertible operator $A + F$, where $\operatorname{rank} F < \infty$. (The sum $A + F$ is in fact the direct sum of the restriction of A to $\operatorname{ran}(1 - E(N))$ and the identity operator on $\operatorname{ran} E(N)$.) Conclusion: A is essentially invertible (because both $1 - A(A+F)^{-1}$ and $1 - (A+F)^{-1}A$ have finite rank).

Suppose now, conversely, that A is essentially left invertible. Atkinson's theorem implies that A has finite nullity and that the restriction of A to $\ker^\perp A$ is invertible. From this, in turn, it follows that if N is the open disc with center 0 and radius equal to the lower bound of A on $\ker^\perp A$, then the range of $E(N)$ is exactly the kernel of A. Conclusion: $\operatorname{rank} E(N) < \infty$. ◄

In a sense the question of essential invertibility for any operator reduces to the question for normal (in fact, positive) operators.

Theorem 14.4. *A necessary and sufficient condition that A be essentially left invertible is that $A^* A$ (or, equivalently, $\sqrt{A^* A}$) be essentially invertible.*

▶ An operator T is essentially left invertible if and only if T^2 is essentially left invertible. Indeed: if $1 - ST^2 = C$, with C compact, then ST is an essential left inverse of T; if, on the other hand, $1 - ST = C$, then $1 - S^2 T^2 = 1 - S(1-C)T = 1 - ST + SCT = C + SCT$, so that S^2 is an essential left inverse of T^2. This proves the equivalence of the left invertibility of A^*A and $\sqrt{A^*A}$.

If now $A = UP$ is the polar decomposition of A $(P = \sqrt{A^*A})$, then $P = U^*A$, so that each of A and P is a left multiple of the other; this makes it obvious that if either one of them is essentially left invertible, then so is the other. ◄

Corollary 14.5. *A necessary and sufficient condition that A be essentially right invertible is that AA^* (or, equivalently, $\sqrt{AA^*}$) be essentially invertible.*

The negation of essential left invertibility is, in geometric terms, equivalent to a strengthening of the condition that 0 be an approximate eigenvalue.

Theorem 14.6. *A necessary and sufficient condition that A not be essentially left invertible is that there exist an orthonormal sequence $\{f_n\}$ such that $\|Af_n\| \to 0$.* [40]

▶ Sufficiency is easy. If $\|Af_n\| \to 0$, and if $1 - BA = C$ with C compact, then $\|f_n - Cf_n\| = \|BAf_n\| \to 0$; since $f_n \to 0$ weakly, the compactness of C implies that $\|Cf_n\| \to 0$, and hence that $\|f_n\| \to 0$, which is a contradiction.

To prove necessity, suppose that A is not essentially left invertible. Theorem 14.4 implies that A^*A is not essentially invertible, and therefore, by Theorem 14.3, the spectral measure E of A^*A evaluated on the intervals $\left[0, \frac{1}{n}\right)$ has infinite rank for every n. Since the restriction of A^*A to the range of $E\left(\left[0, \frac{1}{n}\right)\right)$ is bounded by $\frac{1}{n}$ and since there exists a sequence of integers n_k such that $E\left(\left[\frac{1}{n_{k+1}}, \frac{1}{n_k}\right)\right)$ has non-zero rank, the stated condition follows. ◄

Corollary 14.7. *A necessary and sufficient condition that A not be essentially right invertible is that there exist an orthonormal sequence $\{f_n\}$ such that $\|A^*f_n\| \to 0$.*

Remark 14.8. ▶ Theorem 14.6 sheds some light on Theorem 10.8. What the proof of Theorem 10.8 really proves is that if k is an absolutely bounded kernel on $\mathbb{I} \times \mathbb{I}$, then $\operatorname{Int} k$ is not essentially left invertible. Since k^* is absolutely bounded along with k, it follows that $\operatorname{Int} k$ is not essentially right invertible either. ◄

The definition of invertibility, or, for that matter, of right and left invertibility, makes sense for operators from one space to another, and the same is true about essential invertibility. Atkinson's theorem, and the characterizations of essential invertibility in terms of positive operators and in terms of the images of orthonormal sequences – they all make sense and are true for operators from one space to another. (The characterization of essential invertibility for normal operators is, of course, a single-space theorem.)

Closely related to the concept of invertibility is the concept of spectrum, and that does not make sense for operators from one space to another. Spectra are defined by comparing an operator with a scalar multiple of the identity; if a transformation maps its domain into a different space, it is not comparable with such scalar multiples. It has become traditional, however, to express invertibility in spectral language, even when it is neither necessary nor especially convenient to do so; what follows is a brief description of how the language is used.

The *resolvent set* of an element A of a Banach algebra (a complex Banach algebra with unit) is the set of those complex numbers λ for which $A - \lambda$ ($= A - \lambda 1$) has an inverse in the algebra; the *spectrum* of A is the complement of the resolvent set in the complex plane. If the algebra consists of all bounded operators on a Hilbert space, this definition yields the customary operator spectrum.

There is another Banach algebra, besides the algebra of all operators, associated with a Hilbert space H, namely the quotient (called the *Calkin algebra*) obtained by reducing modulo the ideal $\mathscr{K}$ of compact operators. That is: the Calkin algebra is the collection of cosets $A + \mathscr{K}$ (where A is an operator on H); they constitute a Banach algebra in a natural way. Invertibility in the Calkin algebra can only mean one thing: a coset $A + \mathscr{K}$ is right (or left) invertible when there exists a coset $B + \mathscr{K}$ such that $AB + \mathscr{K}$ (or $BA + \mathscr{K}$) = $1 + \mathscr{K}$. In terms of the operators A (rather than the cosets $A + \mathscr{K}$) this says that there exists an operator B such that AB (or BA) $= 1 - C$, with C compact; in other words, it says exactly that A is essentially right (or left) invertible.

Once the concept of invertibility is at hand, the associated concepts of resolvent set and spectrum are defined in terms of it. Thus, for instance, 0 belongs to the *right* (or *left*) *essential spectrum* of an operator A just in case A is not right (or left) invertible modulo $\mathscr{K}$; the *essential spectrum* of A is the spectrum of the coset $A + \mathscr{K}$ in the Calkin algebra. Observe that since $C + \mathscr{K}$ $= \mathscr{K}$ whenever C is compact, the essential spectrum of an operator is not affected by compact perturbation.

Spectra are defined for operators on one Hilbert space, but it is possible and not too misleading to use an expression such as "0 belongs to the left essential spectrum of A" even for transformations A between different Hilbert spaces. The justification is Theorem 14.4, which says that 0 is in the left essential spectrum of A if and only if 0 is in the essential spectrum of A^*A. The condition makes sense for any bounded linear transformation between different Hilbert spaces even though what it is a condition for does not. In what follows, therefore, "0 belongs to the left essential spectrum of A" will be interpreted to mean that A^*A is not essentially left invertible (and, via Corollary 14.5, "0 belongs to the right essential spectrum of A" will be interpreted similarly in terms of AA^*). Caution: the language can be used for the number 0 only.

Remark 14.9. Is the essential spectrum always non-empty? The question is a special case of a more general one: is the spectrum of an element of a Banach algebra always non-empty? The most familiar special case of the general question concerns the spectrum of an operator on a Hilbert space, which is not trivial even for finite-dimensional spaces. The answer is yes in complete generality, and the proof is not too different from the one for operators.[41]

It is high time to make contact with integral operators again. The following result foreshadows some deeper ones to come; it does for some Carleman kernels what (the proof of) Theorem 10.8 does for all absolutely bounded ones.

Theorem 14.10. *If k is a normal Carleman kernel on $\amalg \times \amalg$, then 0 belongs to the essential spectrum of* Int k.

▶ If Int k is essentially invertible, then (Theorem 14.3) Int k is the direct sum of an invertible operator and an operator of finite rank. The latter direct summand is, of course, a Carleman operator; since, by assumption, the direct sum is a Carleman operator, it follows that the invertible direct summand is a Carleman operator also. In view of Corollary 11.7, that is a contradiction. ◀

The best behaved operators are the Hermitian operators on finite-dimensional spaces; for them all spectral questions are clear and the answers are usually easily computable by diagonalization. For Hermitian operators on infinite-dimensional spaces, the facts are different, but they can be obtained "essentially" the same way. The considerations that follow can be used to study the essential spectra of Hermitian operators, and they will also be used below to characterize all possible integral operators.

A diagonal operator on a Hilbert space is one whose matrix with respect to a suitable orthonormal basis is diagonal, or, equivalently, one whose set of eigenvectors includes an orthonormal basis. The most important single fact about Hermitian operators on finite-dimensional spaces is that they satisfy the conditions of this definition, and, correspondingly, the most worrisome single phenomenon in the theory of Hermitian operators on infinite-dimensional spaces is that they may fail to possess any eigenvectors at all.

The spectral theorem is usually a good substitute for diagonalizability. Another substitute, which in some contexts is more usable, is a remarkable theorem of Weyl: it says that every Hermitian operator is "essentially" diagonal. Precisely: if A is a Hermitian operator on a separable Hilbert space, then there exists a diagonal Hermitian operator D such that $A - D$ is compact. This result was improved by von Neumann, both qualitatively and quantitatively; Theorem 14.13 below has come to be known as the *Weyl-von Neumann theorem*. The following lemma is the major tool in its proof.[42]

Lemma 14.11. *If A is a Hermitian operator on a separable Hilbert space, if f is vector in that space, and if $\varepsilon > 0$, then there exists a projection P of finite rank such that $Pf = f$ and*

$$\|(1-P)AP + PA(1-P)\|_2 < \varepsilon.$$

Remark 14.12. Since P has finite rank, the operators $(1-P)AP$ and $PA(1-P)$ have finite rank. It follows that their Hilbert-Schmidt norm is finite; that is the norm that occurs in the statement of the lemma.

If the underlying space is written as the direct sum of ran P and ran$(1-P)$, then every operator has a natural 2×2 matrix representation with respect to that decomposition. The representation of A has PAP and $(1-P)A(1-P)$ on the diagonal and $(1-P)AP$ and $PA(1-P)$ in the other two positions. (That isn't quite right. The top left entry of the matrix of A is not really PAP, but the restriction of PAP to the range of P, and, similarly, the other three entries are the restrictions of the indicated operators to the appropriate subspaces.) The important part of the lemma is the statement that the difference between the representation of A and its diagonal part has small Hilbert-Schmidt norm.

▶ Assume that A is a positive contraction (i.e., $0 \leq A \leq 1$). This is a harmless assumption, involving no loss of generality; just translate and change scale (i.e., replace A by a suitable $\alpha A + \beta$). Then the spectrum of A is in the interval $[0, 1]$, or, equivalently, the spectral measure E of A has that interval for a support.

Let n be a positive integer (to be determined later); write $\lambda_j = \frac{j}{n}$, $j = 0, 1, \ldots, n$; let E_j be the projection $E([\lambda_{j-1}, \lambda_j))$, $1 \leq j < n$; and let E_n be $E([\lambda_{n-1}, 1])$. Every vector in the range of E_j is an approximate eigenvector of A with degree of approximation $\frac{1}{n}$. $\left(\text{That is: if } E_j h = h, \text{ then } \|Ah - \lambda_j h\| \leq \frac{1}{n}\|h\|.\right)$ Let P be the projection whose range is the span of the vectors $E_1 f, \ldots, E_n f$. Since $E_1 + \cdots + E_n = 1$, it follows that $E_1 f + \cdots + E_n f = f$, and therefore that $Pf = f$.

Assume now that $E_j f \neq 0$ for $j = 1, \ldots, n$; if this is not already true, a small change of notation will make it so. (If there are k indices j such that $E_j f = 0$, give the number $n - k$ the new name n, and re-name the E's for which $E_j f \neq 0$ so that their new names are $E_1, \ldots, E_n$.) Let $\{e_1, e_2, \ldots\}$ be an orthonormal basis for the whole space such that $e_j = \frac{E_j f}{\|E_j f\|}$ when $j = 1, \ldots, n$. With respect to that basis the matrix of AP and the matrix of PAP are very near in Hilbert-Schmidt norm. Indeed:
$$\|APe_j - PAPe_j\| \leq \|APe_j - \lambda_j e_j\|, \quad j = 1, \ldots, n$$

(because $PAPe_j$ is the best approximation to APe_j in ran P), and
$$\|APe_j - \lambda_j e_j\| \leq \frac{1}{n}, \quad j = 1, \ldots, n;$$

it follows that the square root of the sum of the squares of the norms of the columns of $AP - PAP$ is not more than
$$\sqrt{n \cdot \frac{1}{n^2}} = \frac{1}{\sqrt{n}}.$$

In other words:
$$\|(1-P)AP\|_2 \leq \frac{1}{\sqrt{n}}.$$

Since A is Hermitian, this implies that
$$\|PA(1-P)\|_2 \leq \frac{1}{\sqrt{n}}.$$

Conclusion: if $n > \dfrac{4}{\varepsilon^2}$, so that $\dfrac{1}{\sqrt{n}} < \dfrac{\varepsilon}{2}$, then

$$\|(1-P)AP + PA(1-P)\|_2 < \varepsilon. \quad \blacktriangleleft$$

Theorem 14.13. *If A is a Hermitian operator on a separable Hilbert space and if $\varepsilon > 0$, then there exists a diagonal Hermitian operator D such that $A - D$ is a Hilbert-Schmidt operator with $\|A - D\|_2 < \varepsilon$.*

▶ The proof applies Lemma 14.11 infinitely often. Suppose that $\{e_1, e_2, \ldots\}$ is an orthonormal basis. Step 1: apply the lemma to the operator A, the vector e_1, and the number $\varepsilon/2$. The result is a projection P_1 of finite rank such that $P_1 e_1 = e_1$ and

$$\|(1-P_1)AP_1 + P_1 A(1-P_1)\|_2 < \frac{\varepsilon}{2}.$$

Step 2: apply the lemma to the operator obtained by restricting $(1-P_1)A(1-P_1)$ to $\mathrm{ran}^\perp P_1$ (i.e., to the compression of A to $\mathrm{ran}^\perp P_1$), the vector $(1-P_1)e_2$, and the number $\varepsilon/4$. Step n: apply the lemma to the compression of A to the orthogonal complement of the $n-1$ finite-dimensional spaces already constructed, the vector obtained by projecting e_n into that orthogonal complement, and the number $\varepsilon/2^n$. The result of the first n steps is a pairwise orthogonal set of projections $P_1, \ldots, P_n$, of finite rank, such that

$$\|(1-P_j)A_j P_j + P_j A_j(1-P_j)\|_2 < \frac{\varepsilon}{2^j}, \text{ where } A_j = \left(1 - \sum_{k=1}^{j-1} P_k\right) A \left(1 - \sum_{k=1}^{j-1} P_k\right)$$

for $j = 1, \ldots, n$. Since e_n is in $\mathrm{ran}\, P_1 \oplus \cdots \oplus \mathrm{ran}\, P_n$, it follows that the pairwise orthogonal finite-dimensional subspaces $\mathrm{ran}\, P_n$, $n = 1, 2, 3, \ldots$, have the entire space for their direct sum. The "block matrix" of A with respect to that direct sum decomposition of the space is the sum of the "block-diagonal" matrix D obtained by replacing all the off-diagonal blocks by 0, and the remainder. Since the blocks on the diagonal of D are Hermitian operators on finite-dimensional spaces, they are diagonal operators, and, consequently, D as a whole is a diagonal operator. The remainder consists of the "rectangular" blocks $(1-P_n)AP_n$ and $P_n A(1-P_n)$, whose total Hilbert-Schmidt norm is dominated by

$$\sum_{n=1}^{\infty} \frac{\varepsilon}{2^n}. \quad \blacktriangleleft$$

This is von Neumann's proof. The theorem has been studied extensively, and some of the attempts to generalize it have been successful. Thus, for instance, it is true that every *normal* operator on a separable Hilbert space is the sum of a diagonal operator and a compact one, and the norm of the compact summand can be made arbitrarily small. This, however, is a generalization of Weyl's theorem, not of von Neumann's sharpening of it; whether that too is generalizable is unknown.

94

Problem 14.14. *Is every normal operator on a separable Hilbert space the sum of a diagonal operator and a Hilbert-Schmidt operator? If so, can the Hilbert-Schmidt norm of the second summand be made arbitrarily small?*

One of the proofs of the Weyl theorem arose in the algebraic context of "quasidiagonal" operators, which has been receiving considerable attention. To motivate the concept, observe that the definition of diagonal operators could have been formulated this way: there exists a pairwise orthogonal total sequence of 1-dimensional subspaces, each of which is invariant under the operator. ("Total" means that their span is the whole space.) If "1-dimensional" is replaced by "finite-dimensional", the result is a definition of *block-diagonal* operators. Equivalently an operator is block-diagonal if its matrix with respect to a total sequence of finite-dimensional subspaces is diagonal. Here is an obvious and useful generalization: an operator is *block-triangular* if its matrix with respect to a sequence of the same kind is upper triangular. The block analogues of Weyl's theorem can be taken as definitions: an operator is *quasidiagonal* if it is the sum of a block-diagonal operator and a compact one, and it is *quasitriangular* if it is the sum of a block-triangular operator and a compact one. (These are not the original definitions, but an early theorem in the subject states that the present definitions and the original ones are equivalent.) What about the von Neumann theorem: can it be extended to quasidiagonal and quasitriangular operators?

Problem 14.15. *Is every quasidiagonal operator the sum of a block-diagonal operator and a Hilbert-Schmidt operator? Is every quasitriangular operator the sum of a block-triangular operator and a Hilbert-Schmidt operator?* It is easy to see that if the answer is yes, then the Hilbert-Schmidt norm of the second summand can be made arbitrarily small. [43]

§15. Characterization

From the point of view of the foundations of the theory of integral operators, the most important question is this: which operators *can* be integral operators? The question refers to unitary equivalence; in precise terms, it asks for a characterization of those operators A on $L^2(X)$ for which there exists a unitary operator U on $L^2(X)$ such that UAU^* is integral.

[To ask for a characterization of those operators on an abstract Hilbert space that can be unitarily represented as integral operators on $L^2(X)$ is not really a generalization at all. Since representability means unitary equivalence, so that the conditions must be unitarily invariant, the domain of the given operator is immaterial; all that matters about it is that it have the same dimension as $L^2(X)$.

There is another possible generalization: if H and K are Hilbert spaces, under what conditions on an operator $A: H \rightarrow K$ do there exist unitary operators $U: K \rightarrow L^2(Y)$ and $V: H \rightarrow L^2(X)$ such that VAU^* is integral? This two-space question is not about the familiar and important concept of unitary equivalence, UAU^*, but about a looser version, VAU^*, of less geometric content. In the sequel only the original one-space problem, about honest unitary equivalence, will be studied.]

For an illuminating example, consider the multiplication operator A on $L^2(\mathbb{I})$ induced by the characteristic function of $(0, \frac{1}{2})$. By Theorem 8.6, the operator A is not integral. As far as unitary equivalence is concerned, however, A is completely characterized as a projection with both rank and nullity equal to $\aleph_0$. Since there does exist a kernel k on $\mathbb{I} \times \mathbb{I}$ for which Int k is such a projection (Example 6.5), it follows that A *can* be an integral operator.

The answer to the representability question clearly depends on the underlying measure space. For the atomic case ($X = \mathbb{Z}$) the facts are known and trivial: every operator on ℓ^2 *is* induced by a matrix (Theorem 7.3) and therefore *can* be induced by a matrix. The remainder of this section presents a satisfactory characterization of the operators that can be integral operators over a not atomic space. (Awkward language, but what can be done? "Non-atomic" means "divisible" to some people.)

Since the problem is to characterize integral operators to within unitary equivalence, the natural way to begin is to examine unitarily invariant properties of integral operators. An example of a property that is *not* unitarily invariant is the $\langle 2, 1 \rangle$ compactness discussed in §13: the underlying measures, and their finiteness, are not Hilbert space concepts at all, but they are unavoidable in the very definition of $\langle 2, 1 \rangle$ compactness. It may be slightly surprising therefore that $\langle 2, 1 \rangle$ compactness plays an important role in what follows; it will be convenient to have some systematic notation for discussing it.

Once a measure space X is fixed, let $\mathscr{B}$ ($=\mathscr{B}(L^2(X))$) be the set of all bounded operators on $L^2(X)$, and let $\mathscr{K}$ ($=\mathscr{K}(L^2(X))$) be the compact ones among them; let $\mathscr{B}_{2,1}$ ($=\mathscr{B}(L^2(X), L^1(X))$) be the set of all bounded operators from $L^2(X)$ to $L^1(X)$, and let $\mathscr{K}_{2,1}$ ($=\mathscr{K}(L^2(X), L^1(X))$) be the compact ones among them. The classically familiar facts are that $\mathscr{B}$ is an algebra and $\mathscr{K}$ is a closed two-sided ideal in it; $\mathscr{B}_{2,1}$ is a vector space, and $\mathscr{K}_{2,1}$ is a closed subset of it invariant under right multiplication by elements of $\mathscr{B}$. (That is: if $A \in \mathscr{K}_{2,1}$ and $B \in \mathscr{B}$, then $AB \in \mathscr{K}_{2,1}$.)

In case the measure in X happens to be finite, there is a natural injection $i_{2,1}$ from $\mathscr{B}$ into $\mathscr{B}_{2,1}$; in the notation of § 13,

$$i_{2,1}(A) = A_{2,1}$$

whenever $A \in \mathscr{B}$. The injection $i_{2,1}$ is continuous (with respect to the norm topologies in $\mathscr{B}$ and $\mathscr{B}_{2,1}$). In this language the statement that an operator A is $\langle 2,1 \rangle$ compact is expressed by the relation

$$A \in i_{2,1}^{-1}(\mathscr{K}_{2,1}).$$

Note that this recaptures the statement that the set of $\langle 2,1 \rangle$ compact operators is closed. Since, moreover,

$$i_{2,1}(AB) = i_{2,1}(A) \cdot B$$

whenever A and B are in $\mathscr{B}$, it follows that the set of $\langle 2,1 \rangle$ compact operators is a right ideal in $\mathscr{B}$.

Theorem 15.1. *If A is a bounded integral operator on $L^2(X)$, where X is not atomic, then 0 belongs to the right essential spectrum of A.*

▶ If $\mu(X)$ is not finite, then use the isomorphism theorem (6.2) to replace X by a space with finite measure. That is, let $\varphi \colon X' \to X$ be an isomorphism, where X' is a finite (and necessarily not atomic) measure space, and let $U \colon L^2(X) \to L^2(X')$ be the induced unitary operator. (An isomorphism such as φ always exists; cf. Example 6.5.) Since the transform UAU^* is a bounded integral operator on $L^2(X')$, it is only a change of notation to assume that $\mu(X)$ is finite in the first place, and in the rest of the proof that assumption is made. In other words, it is now to be proved that 0 belongs to the right essential spectrum of A, under the added assumption that $\mu(X) < \infty$.

With the use of the theory of $\langle 2,1 \rangle$ compactness the proof becomes easy. The set of $\langle 2,1 \rangle$ compact operators is a closed right ideal in $\mathscr{B}$; the existence of a divisible part of positive measure in X implies that that ideal is proper. The proof of this assertion is similar to the proof of Theorem 8.6: it proves, in fact, that if φ is a bounded measurable function that does not vanish almost everywhere on the divisible part of X, then the multiplication operator M_φ is not $\langle 2,1 \rangle$ compact. Here is how it goes. Let X_0 be the divisible part of X; normalize so that $\mu(X_0) = 1$. Let $\{e_n\}$ be an orthonormal sequence in $L^2(X_0)$ (i.e., $e_n \in L^2(X)$ and $e_n = 0$ on $X - X_0$) such that $|e_n(x)| = 1$ almost everywhere on X_0. (Such a sequence exists because X_0 is isomorphic to $\mathbb{II}$.) Since

$$\|(M_\varphi)e_n\|_1 = \int_{X_0} |\varphi e_n| \, d\mu = \int_{X_0} |\varphi| \, d\mu,$$

it follows that $\|(M_\varphi)e_n\|_1$ cannot tend to 0, i.e., that M_φ cannot be $\langle 2,1 \rangle$ compact, unless φ vanishes almost everywhere on X_0.

Since the constant function 1 does not vanish on X_0, it follows, of course, that the identity operator 1 is not in $\mathscr{K}_{2,1}$. Every compact operator on $L^2(X)$ is $\langle 2,1 \rangle$ compact. Since the given integral operator A is $\langle 2,1 \rangle$ compact (Theorem 13.8), it follows that $AB - C$ is $\langle 2,1 \rangle$ compact for every B in $\mathscr{B}$ and every C in $\mathscr{K}$. Consequence: $AB - C \neq 1$, or, equivalently, $AB - 1 \neq C$, for any such B and C. This is exactly the assertion that A is not essentially right invertible. ◄

Remark 15.2. Why *right* and not *left*? What causes the lack of symmetry? A part of the answer is that right and left are far from the best terms to apply to the factors in the composite of two mappings; "pre" and "post" would be much more descriptive. Why then does the essential "prespectrum" play a role, instead of the essential "postspectrum"? The answer is that the operators being studied have a compactness property, and compactness is defined in terms of the range of an operator. A compact operator has a small range, and so therefore has any product in which it occurs last. No matter what *precedes*, an application of a compact operator squeezes the range; the resulting composite cannot be anywhere near the identity.

The property of $\langle 2,1 \rangle$ compactness is not a unitarily invariant one, but it implies that 0 is in the right essential spectrum, and *that* is a unitarily invariant property. Theorem 15.1 can therefore be expressed as follows.

Corollary 15.3. *If X is not atomic, and if an operator A on $L^2(X)$ is unitarily equivalent to an integral operator, then 0 belongs to the right essential spectrum of A.*

Note, incidentally, that Theorem 15.1 supersedes the earlier non-invertibility results Theorem 10.8 (about absolutely bounded kernels), Corollary 11.7 (about Carleman kernels), and Theorem 14.10 (about normal Carleman kernels). Note also that Corollary 15.3 answers, negatively, the question of representability by integral operators over divisible spaces for large classes of operators. Thus, for instance, no invertible operator can be an integral operator on $L^2(\mathbb{R}_+)$, and neither can any unilateral shift of finite multiplicity. (If U is a unilateral shift of multiplicity n, then $1 - UU^*$ is a projection of rank n, so that U^* is an essential right inverse of U.) As far as the representability of a unilateral shift of infinite multiplicity is concerned, Corollary 15.3 has nothing to say; cf. Example 15.9.

The best thing about the necessary condition of Corollary 15.3 is that it is also sufficient. A convenient way to begin the proof of sufficiency is to look at the operators for which 0 is in the essential spectrum the easy way, namely the operators A that have a "large 0 direct summand". The expression means that the domain of A is a direct sum $H \oplus K$ such that both H and K reduce A, $\dim H \leq \dim K$, and the restriction of A to K is 0. Equivalently, the null-space (kernel) of A includes a reducing subspace whose dimension is at least half the dimension of the whole space.

Lemma 15.4. *If H is a Hilbert space of dimension $\aleph_0$, if A is a bounded operator of the form $B \oplus 0$ on $H \oplus H$, if b is the matrix of B with respect to an orthonormal basis of H, and if k is the inflation of b to a kernel on $\mathbb{R}_+ \times \mathbb{R}_+$, then A is unitarily equivalent to Int k.*

98

▶ The inflation of b is the tensor product $b \otimes k'$, where k' is the kernel on $\mathbb{I} \times \mathbb{I}$ defined by $k'(x, y) = 1$ for all x and y (Example 9.8). Since $\operatorname{Int} k'$ is a projection of rank 1 (cf. Example 5.1), so that $\operatorname{Int} k' = 1 \oplus 0$, where the domains of 1 and 0 are subspaces of dimensions 1 and $\aleph_0$ respectively, it follows that

$$\operatorname{Int}(b \otimes k') = \operatorname{Int} b \otimes \operatorname{Int} k' = B \otimes (1 \oplus 0) = (B \otimes 1) \oplus 0;$$

(cf. the discussion of distributive laws at the beginning of §14). Conclusion: if $k = b \otimes k'$, then $\operatorname{Int} k$ is unitarily equivalent to A. ◀

Remark 15.5. ▶ The lemma is, of course, applicable to all divisible measure spaces in the role of $\mathbb{R}_+$. (An inflation k of b to $X \times X$ is given by a definition of the form

$$k(x, y) = \sum_i \sum_j b(i, j) \frac{1}{\sqrt{\mu(E_i)}} \frac{1}{\sqrt{\mu(E_j)}} \chi_{E_i}(x) \chi_{E_j}(y),$$

where $\{E_1, E_2, E_3, \ldots\}$ is a partition of the divisible measure space X by sets of finite positive measure.) It is often good to know that the lemma is applicable to all not atomic (but not necessarily divisible) measure spaces as well. Indeed, if X is a measure space with a non-empty divisible subset X_0, and if k_0 is a bounded kernel on $X_0 \times X_0$, then let k be the direct sum of k_0 and the zero kernel on $(X - X_0) \times (X - X_0)$. The kernel k is bounded, of course; $\operatorname{Int} k$ is, in fact, the direct sum of $\operatorname{Int} k_0$ and the operator 0 on $L^2(X - X_0)$. If $\operatorname{Int} k_0$ has a large 0 direct summand, then $\operatorname{Int} k (= \operatorname{Int} k_0 \oplus 0)$ is unitarily equivalent to $\operatorname{Int} k_0$; the 0 direct summand of $\operatorname{Int} k_0$ can absorb the additional 0 direct summand of $\operatorname{Int} k$. Conclusion: an operator with large 0 direct summand is representable by either an inflated matrix, or the direct sum of an inflated matrix and 0, over any not atomic space. ◀

The Weyl-von Neumann theorem can be used to show that operators that have a large 0 direct summand are not so rare as they might appear to be.

Lemma 15.6. *If A is a Hermitian operator (on a Hilbert space of dimension $\aleph_0$) that has 0 in its essential spectrum, then there exists a Hermitian Hilbert-Schmidt operator C such that $A - C$ (is diagonal and) has a large 0 direct summand.*

▶ By the Weyl-von Neumann theorem (14.13), $A = D + C_0$, where D is a diagonal Hermitian operator and C_0 is a Hilbert-Schmidt operator. Since 0 is in the essential spectrum of A, therefore 0 is in the essential spectrum of D, so that 0 is a limit point of the sequence of eigenvalues of D. Find a square summable infinite subsequence of those eigenvalues, and let C_1 be the operator obtained from D by replacing all the eigenvalues not in that subsequence by 0. (That is: if D corresponds to the matrix diag $\langle \delta_1, \delta_2, \delta_3, \ldots \rangle$, then C_1 corresponds, in the same basis, to diag $\langle \gamma_1, \gamma_2, \gamma_3, \ldots \rangle$, where $\gamma_n = \delta_n$ for the terms of the subsequence and $\gamma_n = 0$ otherwise.) If $C = C_0 + C_1$, then C is a Hilbert-Schmidt operator and $A - C$ has a large 0 direct summand. ◀

Theorem 15.7. *If a bounded operator A on $L^2(X)$ has 0 in its right essential spectrum, then A is unitarily equivalent to a Carleman operator on $L^2(X)$.*

▶ If X is atomic, the conclusion is true with no spectral assumption. Assume, therefore, that X is not atomic.

If A is Hermitian, then, by Lemma 15.6, $A=D+C$, where D is a Hermitian operator with a large 0 direct summand and C is a Hilbert-Schmidt operator. By Lemma 15.4 (cf. also Remark 15.5), the operator D is unitarily equivalent to an integral operator whose kernel is either the inflation of a bounded matrix or the direct sum of such an inflation and the zero kernel contributed by the atomic part of X. Since a bounded matrix is a Carleman kernel, the same is true of its inflation. The unitary operator U that carries D onto a Carleman operator UDU^* on $L^2(X)$ carries the Hilbert-Schmidt operator C onto some Hilbert-Schmidt operator on $L^2(X)$. Since a Hilbert-Schmidt operator is always an integral operator (and, of course, a Carleman operator), it follows that UCU^* is a Carleman operator on $L^2(X)$, and, therefore, so is $UAU^*=UDU^*+UCU^*$. For Hermitian operators the proof is complete.

For general bounded operators the result can be inferred from the right-ideal theorem (11.6). Given A, consider its left-handed polar decomposition $A=PU$, so that P is Hermitian (in fact positive) and has 0 in its essential spectrum. Since, by the preceding paragraph, P is unitarily equivalent to a Carleman operator on $L^2(X)$, the right-ideal theorem yields the same conclusion for A. ◀⁴⁴

The statement of Theorem 15.7 implies that if $\varphi(x)=x$ for x in $\mathbb{I}$, then M_φ (the "position operator" on $L^2(\mathbb{I})$) is representable as a Carleman operator on $L^2(\mathbb{I})$. What does a Carleman representation of it look like?

Corollary 15.8. *A bounded operator on $L^2(X)$, where X is a not atomic measure space, is unitarily equivalent to an integral operator on $L^2(X)$ if and only if it is unitarily equivalent to a Carleman operator on $L^2(X)$.*

The statement of Corollary 15.8 is an immediate consequence of Corollary 15.3 and Theorem 15.7, but its geometric and analytic content are far from obvious. The statement implies, for instance, that the Abel operator (Example 5.3), which is not a Carleman operator on $L^2(\mathbb{I})$, is unitarily equivalent to one. What does a Carleman representation of it look like?

Theorem 15.7 implies that a unilateral shift of multiplicity $\aleph_0$ is representable as a Carleman operator on $L^2(\mathbb{R}_+)$. What does a Carleman representation of it look like?

Example 15.9. If U is a unilateral shift of multiplicity $\aleph_0$ and if B is an arbitrary bounded operator, then $1-B^*U^*$ agrees with the identity on an infinite-dimensional subspace, and therefore cannot be compact; it follows that the adjoint $1-UB$ cannot be compact either, so that 0 is in the right essential spectrum of U. Theorem 15.7 implies that U is unitarily equivalent to a Carleman operator on $L^2(\mathbb{R}_+)$; it is instructive to examine a concrete Carleman representation of U.

Note: the general theory says and this example illustrates that *left* invertibility is no obstacle to Carleman representability over not atomic spaces. Cf. also Example 9.7.

▶ The polar decomposition of U^* is $U^*(UU^*)$; the partially isometric factor is U^* and the positive factor is the projection UU^*. It is easy to represent UU^* as a Carleman operator on $\mathbb{R}_+ \times \mathbb{R}_+$; a suitable kernel is given by

$$k_0(x,y)=\sum_{n=1}^\infty \chi_n(x)\chi_n(y),$$

where $\chi_n = \chi_{[n-1,n)}$, $n = 1, 2, 3, \ldots$; cf. Example 5.1. The corresponding Carleman function is given, as always, by

$$\gamma_0(x) = \overline{k_0(x,\cdot)} \, (= k_0(x,\cdot)),$$

so that

$$\gamma_0(x) = \chi_n \quad \text{if } x \in [n-1,n), \ n = 1, 2, 3, \ldots.$$

In this representation of UU^* the range is spanned by the functions $\chi_1, \chi_2, \chi_3, \ldots$. To get a representation of U, extend the orthonormal set $\{\chi_1, \chi_2, \chi_3, \ldots\}$ to an orthonormal basis in a completely arbitrary manner. Suppose, to be specific, that $\{f_1, f_2, f_3, \ldots\} \cup \{\chi_1, \chi_2, \chi_3, \ldots\}$ is an orthonormal basis for $L^2(\mathbb{R}_+)$; one of the many ways to represent U then is by the action indicated in the diagram:

(∗)
$$\begin{cases} f_1 \to \chi_1 \to \chi_2 \to \chi_4 \to \chi_7 \to \cdots \\ f_2 \to \chi_3 \to \chi_5 \to \chi_8 \to \cdots \\ f_3 \to \chi_6 \to \chi_9 \to \cdots \\ f_4 \to \chi_{10} \to \cdots \\ \cdots \end{cases}$$

Since $U = (UU^*)U$, the right-ideal theorem (11.6) implies that the Carleman function γ of U is given by

$$\gamma = U^* \gamma_0.$$

It follows that γ is defined as indicated in the diagram:

	χ_1		χ_2	χ_3		χ_4	χ_5	χ_6		χ_7
f_1		f_2			f_3			f_4		
0	1	2	3	4	5	6	7	8	9	10	11

(Caution: the diagram does *not* indicate that the value of $\gamma(x)$ is $f_3(x)$ in $[5,6)$. It indicates that if $x \in [5,6)$, then the value of $\gamma(x)$ is the vector f_3 in $L^2(\mathbb{R}_+)$.)

It is easy to reconcile the definition of U that this implies with the one given by (∗) above, thus:

$$Uf_1(x) = (f_1, \gamma(x)) = \begin{cases} (f_1, f_1) & \text{for } x \text{ in } [0,1) \\ 0 & \text{otherwise} \end{cases} = \chi_1(x),$$

$$U\chi_1(x) = (\chi_1, \gamma(x)) = \begin{cases} (\chi_1, \chi_1) & \text{for } x \text{ in } [1,2) \\ 0 & \text{otherwise} \end{cases} = \chi_2(x),$$

$$Uf_2(x) = (f_2, \gamma(x)) = \begin{cases} (f_2, f_2) & \text{for } x \text{ in } [2,3) \\ 0 & \text{otherwise} \end{cases} = \chi_3(x),$$

$$U\chi_2(x) = (\chi_2, \gamma(x)) = \begin{cases} (\chi_2, \chi_2) & \text{for } x \text{ in } [3,4) \\ 0 & \text{otherwise} \end{cases} = \chi_4(x),$$

etc. ◄

The algebraic structure of the set of Carleman representable operators (over a not atomic measure space) is not rich; here are some small comments.

(1) If A and B are representable as Carleman operators, $A + B$ may fail to be so representable. For an example, write $A = \begin{pmatrix} 1 & 0 \\ 0 & 0 \end{pmatrix}$ and $B = \begin{pmatrix} 0 & 0 \\ 0 & 1 \end{pmatrix}$, where the entries 0 and 1 are to be interpreted as operators on an infinite-dimensional Hilbert space. Since each of A and B has 0 in its right essential spectrum, it follows that both A and B are representable as Carleman operators; since, however, $A + B$ is the identity, $A + B$ is not so representable.

(2) If A is representable as a Carleman operator and if B is any bounded operator, then AB is representable. Reason: if 0 is in the right essential spectrum of A, then 0 is in the right essential spectrum of AB.

(3) If A is representable as a Carleman operator and if B is invertible, then BA is representable. Reason: if $BAD = 1 + C$, with C compact, then $ADB = B^{-1}(BAD)B = 1 + B^{-1}CB$, so that if 0 is not in the right essential spectrum of BA, then 0 is not in the right essential spectrum of AD, and hence not in the right essential spectrum of A. Caution: this does not say that the set of Carleman operators is a left ideal, nor even that if A is a Carleman operator and B is left invertible, then BA is a Carleman operator. Example: let A be a left invertible Carleman operator, with left inverse B. The operator B is, to be sure, not invertible, but, since every operator is a linear combination of four unitary operators, it follows that there exist Carleman operators A and unitary operators U such that UA is not a Carleman operator.[45]

Can there be an operator A such that A is unitarily equivalent to an integral operator on $L^2(X)$ but A^* is not? The mere fact that for some X's there can exist an integral operator on $L^2(X)$ whose adjoint is not an integral operator on the same $L^2(X)$ doesn't answer the question. The unilateral shift U of infinite multiplicity does answer the question: the right essential spectrum of U does contain 0, but, because $U^*U = 1$, the right essential spectrum of U^* does not.

What happens if 0 belongs to the right essential spectra of both A and A^*, so that both A and A^* are unitarily equivalent to integral operators on $L^2(X)$? Does it follow that they are *simultaneously* unitarily equivalent to integral operators on $L^2(X)$? Does it follow, in other words, that there exists *one* unitary operator U such that *both* UAU^* and UA^*U^* are integral operators on $L^2(X)$? The answer is no.

Example 15.10. ▶ Let H be an infinite-dimensional Hilbert space, and let A be the operator on $H \oplus H$ whose matrix is $\begin{pmatrix} 0 & 0 \\ 1 & 0 \end{pmatrix}$. Since $A^2 = 0$, it follows that 0 belongs to the right (and also to the left) essential spectrum of A. Indeed: if not, i.e., if $AB = 1 + C$, where B is bounded and C is compact, then (multiply by A on the left) $0 = A + AC$, whence A is compact $(= -AC)$, which is not true. (Alternatively: since AA^* has the operator 0 on H as a direct summand, the number 0 belongs to the right essential spectrum of A; cf. Corollary 14.5). It follows (by a similar reasoning, or by an application of the corresponding left fact for A) that 0 belongs to the right essential spectrum of A^*. Consequence: both A and A^* are unitarily equivalent to integral operators on, say, $L^2(\mathbb{I})$. Assertion: the unitary equivalences cannot be simultaneous. Reason: $A + A^*$ is invertible. If both UAU^* and UA^*U^* were integral operators on $L^2(\text{II})$, then their sum would be one too, but that's something an invertible operator cannot be. ◄

In view of the preceding discussion and example, it is natural to ask for a characterization of those operators A on $L^2(X)$ for which there exists a unitary operator U on $L^2(X)$ such that both UAU^* and UA^*U^* are integral. If X is atomic, no conditions are needed: every A will do. For not atomic spaces it turns out that there is a simple and satisfactory answer that resembles in several respects the characterization of the operators that can be integral.

Theorem 15.11. *If both A and A^* are bounded integral operators on $L^2(X)$, where X is not atomic, then 0 belongs to the essential spectrum of $A^*A + AA^*$.*

▶ Assume, with no loss, that $\mu(X) < \infty$. Then both A and A^* are $\langle 2, 1 \rangle$ compact, and, therefore, so is $A^*A + AA^*$. The conclusion follows as in Theorem 15.1. ◄

Corollary 15.12. *If X is not atomic, if A is a bounded operator on $L^2(X)$, and if U is a unitary operator such that both UAU^* and UA^*U^* are integral operators on $L^2(X)$, then 0 belongs to the essential spectrum of $A^*A + AA^*$.*

For the converse of Theorem 15.11 (to within unitary equivalence) it is convenient to derive a consequence of its conclusion, a consequence that has more than one application.

Lemma 15.13. *If A is a bounded operator on $L^2(X)$ such that 0 is in the essential spectrum of $A^*A + AA^*$, then A is the sum of an operator with a large 0 direct summand and a Hilbert-Schmidt operator.*

▶ By Corollary 14.7, there exists an orthonormal sequence $\{f_n\}$ such that $\|(A^*A + AA^*)f_n\| < \dfrac{1}{2^n}$. It follows that

$$\sum_n (\|Af_n\|^2 + \|A^*f_n\|^2) = \sum_n ((A^*A + AA^*)f_n, f_n)$$

$$\leq \sum_n \|(A^*A + AA^*)f_n\| < \infty.$$

If, therefore, Q is the projection onto the span of the f_n's, then both AQ and QA ($=(A^*Q)^*$) are Hilbert-Schmidt operators. If $P = 1 - Q$, then

$$A = PAP + (PAQ + QAP + QAQ);$$

the first term has a large 0 direct summand, and the last three are Hilbert-Schmidt operators. In matrix language: consider the decomposition $L^2(X) = \text{ran } P \oplus \text{ran}^\perp P$, and the corresponding matrix $\begin{pmatrix} D & E \\ F & G \end{pmatrix}$ for A. Since the matrices corresponding to AQ and QA are $\begin{pmatrix} 0 & E \\ 0 & G \end{pmatrix}$ and $\begin{pmatrix} 0 & 0 \\ F & G \end{pmatrix}$, it follows that E, F, and G are Hilbert-

Schmidt operators, and hence that A is the sum of an operator with a large 0 direct summand (namely $D \oplus 0$) and a Hilbert-Schmidt operator. ◄

Theorem 15.14. *If A is a bounded operator on $L^2(X)$ such that 0 is in the essential spectrum of $A^*A + AA^*$, then there exists a unitary operator U such that both UAU^* and UA^*U^* are Carleman operators on $L^2(X)$.*

▶ Assume, with no loss, that X is not atomic. By Lemma 15.14, A is the sum of an operator of the form $D \oplus 0$, with a large 0, and a Hilbert-Schmidt operator. By Lemma 15.4 and Remark 15.5, there is a unitary operator U that transforms $D \oplus 0$ to Int k, where k is either an inflated matrix or the direct sum of an inflated matrix and a zero kernel. In either case, both k and its conjugate transpose kernel are bounded Carleman kernels, and therefore (Theorem 7.5) (Int k)*, which is the transform by U of $D^* \oplus 0$, is a Carleman operator. As for the Hilbert-Schmidt summand: transform it too by U, and then use the fact that a Hilbert-Schmidt operator is always a Carleman operator. ◄

Corollary 15.15. *For a bounded operator A on $L^2(X)$, where X is not atomic, there exists a unitary operator U such that both UAU^* and UA^*U^* are integral operators on $L^2(X)$ if and only if there exists a unitary operator V such that both VAV^* and VA^*V^* are Carleman operators on $L^2(X)$.*[46]

Representability questions can be asked for many classes of kernels. The preceding work set out to answer one but ended up answering four (bounded kernels, Carleman kernels, the k's such that both k and $k*$ are bounded kernels, and the k's such that both k and $k*$ are Carleman kernels). Others remain, but knowledge about them is either non-existent or fragmentary. Here, for instance, is a question about which nothing is known.

Problem 15.16. *Under what conditions on an operator A on $L^2(X)$, where X is atomic, is A unitarily equivalent to Int k with k absolutely bounded?* It isn't even known whether any conditions are needed at all. In other words: *does every operator have an absolutely bounded matrix?*

About the absolutely bounded characterization question over not atomic spaces something is known, but not very much.

Theorem 15.17. *If X is not atomic, and if an operator A on $L^2(X)$ is unitarily equivalent to an integral operator on $L^2(X)$ with absolutely bounded kernel, then 0 belongs to the essential spectrum of $A^*A + AA^*$.*

▶ Assume, with no loss, that $A =$ Int k, with k absolutely bounded. By Corollary 10.6, $k*$ is an absolutely bounded kernel and Int $k* = A^*$; the conclusion follows from Theorem 15.11. ◄

The next result is even more meager, but it deserves mention because of its curious relation to Problem 15.16: if every operator does have an absolutely bounded matrix, then the spectral condition in Theorem 15.17 is sufficient as well as necessary.

Theorem 15.18. *If an operator A on $L^2(X)$ has an absolutely bounded matrix, and if 0 belongs to the essential spectrum of $A^*A + AA^*$, then A is unitarily equivalent to a Carleman operator on $L^2(X)$ with absolutely bounded kernel.*

▶ The proof is similar to that of Theorem 15.14. Assume that X is not atomic, and use the spectral assumption to infer (via Lemma 15.13) that there is a Hilbert-Schmidt operator C such that $A - C$ has a large 0 direct summand. The Hilbert-Schmidt operator C can be carried along, as usual, and then represented as a Carleman operator with absolutely bounded kernel at the end; there is, therefore, no loss of generality in assuming that it isn't even present.

If $A = B \oplus 0$, with a large 0, incorporate "half" of that 0 into B, and assume therefore that B itself has a large 0 direct summand. It follows then that A and B are unitarily equivalent, and hence that B has an absolutely bounded matrix b. Lemma 15.4 can be used to represent A as Int k, where k is the inflation of b or the direct sum of that inflation and a zero kernel. In either case, k is an absolutely bounded Carleman kernel. ◀

§16. Universality

Which operators *must* be integral operators? As in §15, this question too refers to unitary equivalence, but this time with the universal quantifier instead of the existential one. In precise terms: under what conditions on an operator A on $L^2(X)$ does it happen that UAU^* is an integral operator for every unitary U on $L^2(X)$? When it does happen, the operator A will be called a *universal* integral operator on $L^2(X)$.

Are there any universal integral operators? The answer is yes, and trivially so. If X is atomic, then every (bounded) operator on $L^2(X)$ is a Carleman operator, and therefore a universal integral operator. There are also less trivial examples: no matter what X is, every Hilbert-Schmidt operator is universal. The principal result of this section is the following converse.

Theorem 16.1. *If A is a universal integral operator on $L^2(X)$, where X is not atomic, then A is a Hilbert-Schmidt operator.*

▶ Assume, with no loss, that $\mu(X) < \infty$.

(1) The first step is to prove that A is compact. For this purpose, apply the Weyl-von Neumann theorem (14.13) to conclude that the Hermitian operator AA^* is a sum $D + C$, where D is diagonal and C is a Hilbert-Schmidt operator. It would be good to know that D too is a universal integral operator (at this stage of the proof it is not known to be an integral operator at all), but, failing that, the next best thing is to note that D is $\langle 2, 1 \rangle$ compact. Reason: A is $\langle 2, 1 \rangle$ compact (13.8), C is $\langle 2, 1 \rangle$ compact, $D = AA^* - C$, and the $\langle 2, 1 \rangle$ compact operators form a right ideal. Since both classes of operators (universally integral and Hilbert-Schmidt) are unitarily invariant, the reasoning can be applied to any unitary transform of A; it yields the conclusion that if U is unitary, then UDU^* is $\langle 2, 1 \rangle$ compact.

Let X_0 be a divisible set of positive measure in X such that the complement $X_1 = X - X_0$ (which contains all the atoms) also includes a divisible set of positive measure (i.e., X_1 does not consist of the atoms alone). It now becomes convenient to normalize the measure so that $\mu(X_0) = 1$. Then there exists an orthonormal basis $\{e_n\}$ for $L^2(X_0)$ such that $|e_n(x)| = 1$ almost everywhere in X_0. Let $\{f_n\}$ be an arbitrary orthonormal basis for $L^2(X_1)$. Distribute the eigenvalues of D, half to the e's and half to the f's; in other words, consider operators D_0 and D_1 such that $D_0 e_n = \alpha_n e_n$, $D_1 f_n = \beta_n f_n$, and $D_0 \oplus D_1$ is unitarily equivalent to D. Note that, by the preceding paragraph, $D_0 \oplus D_1$ is $\langle 2, 1 \rangle$ compact, and hence that both D_0 and D_1 are $\langle 2, 1 \rangle$ compact.

Since $e_n \to 0$ weakly, it follows that $D_0 e_n \to 0$ in $L^1(X_0)$; since

$$\|D_0 e_n\|_1 = \int |\alpha_n e_n(x)| \, dx = |\alpha_n|,$$

it follows that D_0 is compact. Interchange the roles of the α's and the β's to infer that $\beta_n \to 0$ and hence that D_1 is compact. (The interchange can be effected by a change of notation — redefine D_0 so that, this time, $D_0 e_n = \beta_n e_n$ — or, alternatively, by transforming $D_0 \oplus D_1$ by the unitary operator on $L^2(X)$ that interchanges e_n and f_n for each n.) Consequence: D is compact.

Since D is compact, so also is $AA^* (= D + C)$, and hence (polar decomposition) so is A.

(2) Since A is compact, and since the compact operators form a two-sided ideal, it follows that $A^* A + A A^*$ is compact, and hence that 0 belongs to the essential spectrum of $A^* A + A A^*$. Apply Lemma 15.13 to infer that A is the sum of a Hilbert-Schmidt operator and an operator with a large 0 direct summand. Split X, as in step (1) above, into X_0 and X_1; it follows that A is unitarily equivalent to the sum of a Hilbert-Schmidt operator and a direct sum of the form $B \oplus 0$ defined on $L^2(X_0) \oplus L^2(X_1)$. The purpose of the rest of the proof, therefore, is to show that B is a Hilbert-Schmidt operator. Since the Hilbert-Schmidt summand of A is universal, what is already known is that $B \oplus 0$ is a universal integral operator. The next step in the proof is to show that B satisfies a much stronger condition: namely, if P and Q are arbitrary operators (on $L^2(X_0)$), then PBQ is an integral operator on $L^2(X_0)$.

An arbitrary contraction P on $L^2(X_0)$ has a unitary dilation to $L^2(X)$. In other words, corresponding to P there exists a unitary operator U on $L^2(X)$ such that the matrix of U with respect to the decomposition $L^2(X) = L^2(X_0) \oplus L^2(X_1)$ is of the form $\begin{pmatrix} P & R \\ S & T \end{pmatrix}$. (Here T is an operator on $L^2(X_1)$, R maps $L^2(X_1)$ to $L^2(X_0)$, and S goes in the other direction.) Since the transform of $B \oplus 0$ by U is an integral operator, there exists a kernel k on $X \times X$ such that $U(B \oplus 0) U^* = \text{Int } k$. The subkernel obtained by restricting k to $X_0 \times X_0$ is a bounded kernel; the operator it induces is the compression of $U(B \oplus 0) U^*$ to $L^2(X_0)$. Since

$$\begin{pmatrix} P & R \\ S & T \end{pmatrix} \begin{pmatrix} B & 0 \\ 0 & 0 \end{pmatrix} \begin{pmatrix} P^* & S^* \\ R^* & T^* \end{pmatrix} = \begin{pmatrix} PBP^* & * \\ * & * \end{pmatrix},$$

it follows that PBP^* is an integral operator on $L^2(X_0)$ for every contraction P; since every operator is a scalar multiple of a contraction, it follows that PBP^* is an integral operator on $L^2(X_0)$ for every operator P. This condition is obviously and automatically unitarily invariant. If, that is, U is an arbitrary unitary operator on $L^2(X_0)$, then $P(UBU^*)P^*$ is an integral operator on $L^2(X_0)$ for every operator P.

Apply the result just obtained to $P + \lambda$ instead of P to obtain the result that

$$(P + \lambda) B (P + \lambda)^* = PBP^* + |\lambda|^2 B + \bar{\lambda} PB + \lambda BP^*$$

is always an integral operator. Since PBP^* and $|\lambda|^2 B$ are integral operators, it follows that so also is $\bar{\lambda} PB + \lambda BP^*$ for every λ. Put $\lambda = 1$ and $\lambda = i$. Consequence: both

$$PB + BP^* \quad \text{and} \quad PB - BP^*$$

are integral operators, and, therefore, so also are PB and BP^*. Since B can be replaced by any operator unitarily equivalent to it, it follows that UBU^*P^* is an integral operator whenever U is unitary. Given any operator Q, and any unitary operator U, apply the preceding sentence to Q^*U^* in place of P to infer that UBQ is an integral operator. Since, finally, P is a linear combination of four unitary operators (and every linear combination of integral operators is an integral operator), it follows that PBQ is an integral operator; step (2) is complete.

(3) The situation now is this: X_0 is a divisible measure space with measure 1, B is a compact operator on $L^2(X_0)$, and all products of operators on $L^2(X_0)$ that have B as a factor are integral operators on $L^2(X_0)$. The object is to prove that B is a Hilbert-Schmidt operator.

If $B = U_0 P_0$ is the polar decomposition of B, then $U_0^* B_0 = P_0$. Since P_0 inherits the two properties of B described in the preceding paragraph, the remainder of the proof proceeds under the assumption that B was Hermitian to begin with.

The compact Hermitian operator B has an orthonormal basis consisting of eigenvectors. Find a unitary operator that sends that basis onto the basis $\{e_n\}$ of functions of constant absolute value, used in step (1). The transform of B by that unitary operator has the e's as eigenvectors; since the transform has all the properties of B, the rest of the proof assumes that $Be_n = \lambda_n e_n$ for suitable scalars λ_n. (The compactness of B implies that $\lambda_n \to 0$, but that turns out not to be of any help in what follows.) The proof that B is a Hilbert-Schmidt operator, i.e., that $\sum_n |\lambda_n|^2 < \infty$, will be accomplished by showing that $\sum_n |\alpha_n \lambda_n| < \infty$ for every sequence α in ℓ^2.

To do that, the proof uses an arbitrarily prescribed sequence α in ℓ^2 to construct a function f in $L^2(X_0)$ and derives the desired conclusion by an examination of the relation between f and B.

The divisibility of X_0 implies the existence in X_0 of a disjoint sequence $\{E_n\}$ of sets of positive measure. If $f_n = \dfrac{1}{\sqrt{\mu(E_n)}} \chi_{E_n}$, then the f's form an orthonormal sequence with disjoint supports. Define f by

$$f = \sum_n \alpha_n f_n;$$

the series converges in every pertinent sense (in L^2, everywhere, absolutely). The orthogonality of $\{f_n\}$ implies the existence of an operator V on $L^2(X_0)$ (in fact an isometry) such that $Ve_n = f_n$ for all n; the strong form of the universality of B implies the existence of a kernel k_0 on $X_0 \times X_0$ such that $BV^* = \text{Int } k_0$. Since k_0 is bounded and $f \in L^2(X_0)$, it follows that

$$\int_{X_0} |k_0(x,y)f(y)|\, dy < \infty$$

for almost every x. This in turn implies that

$$\infty > \sum_n |\alpha_n| \int_{X_0} |k_0(x,y)f_n(y)|\, dy \geq \sum_n |\alpha_n| \left| \int_{X_0} k_0(x,y)f_n(y)\, dy \right|$$

$$= \sum_n |\alpha_n| \cdot |BV^* f_n(x)| = \sum_n |\alpha_n| \cdot |Be_n(x)| = \sum_n |\alpha_n| \cdot |\lambda_n|. \quad \blacktriangleleft$$

Remark 16.2. ▶ The original form of Theorem 16.1 obtained the same conclusion under a stronger assumption, namely the assumption that A is a universal Carleman operator on $L^2(X)$. (Meaning: UAU^* is a Carleman operator on $L^2(X)$ whenever U is unitary on $L^2(X)$.) The main idea of the proof for the Carleman case is most clearly seen for diagonal operators A on $L^2(\mathbb{I})$. If the eigenvalues of A are λ_n ($n = 0, \pm 1, \pm 2, \dots$, for convenience), let B be the diagonal operator on $L^2(\mathbb{I})$ defined by $B e_n = \lambda_n e_n$ ($n = 0, \pm 1, \pm 2, \dots$), where $\{e_n\}$ is the usual exponential basis. Since B is unitarily equivalent to A, the universal Carleman assumption yields a Carleman function γ such that $B g(x) = (g, \gamma(x))$ whenever $g \in L^2(\mathbb{I})$. Consequence: $B e_n(x)$ is the complex conjugate of the n-th Fourier coefficient of $\gamma(x)$ for almost every x, and therefore $\sum_n |B e_n(x)|^2 < \infty$; this inequality implies that $\sum_n |\lambda_n|^2 < \infty$. ◀[47]

Universality was defined by requiring something of *every* unitary operator; what happens if the requirement is placed on sufficiently "small" unitary operators only?

Problem 16.3. ▶ *If A is an operator on $L^2(X)$, and if there exists a positive number ε such that UAU^* is an integral operator whenever U is a unitary operator on $L^2(X)$ and $\|U - 1\| < \varepsilon$, does it follow that A is a Hilbert-Schmidt operator?* The hypothesis about small unitary transforms is (apparently) not invariant under unitary equivalence; a related unitarily invariant question goes as follows. *If A is an operator on $L^2(X)$ and if A is not a Hilbert-Schmidt operator, can the set of unitary operators that transform A into an integral operator have a non-empty interior?* (The topological expression refers to the space of all unitary operators equipped with the norm topology.) ◀[48]

At least one interesting universality question is not answered by Theorem 16.1; it concerns absolutely bounded matrices. One way to formulate the question is this: which matrices are *universally absolutely bounded*? Equivalently: which operators A on ℓ^2 have the property that the matrix of UAU^* is absolutely bounded for every unitary U on ℓ^2? (The consideration of atomic measure spaces is unavoidable here; for spaces that are not atomic the answer is included in Theorem 16.1.)

A Hilbert-Schmidt matrix is absolutely bounded, and, since the Hilbert-Schmidt property is unitarily invariant, it is universally absolutely bounded. The Hilbert-Schmidt matrices cannot, however, be the only ones that are universally absolutely bounded; the scalars (i.e., scalar multiples of the identity matrix) are additional examples (and, as such, they have no analogues in the not atomic case). Since a sum of two universally absolutely bounded matrices is another one, every matrix of the form $\lambda + h$, where λ is a scalar and h is a Hilbert-Schmidt matrix, is universally absolutely bounded. Theorem 16.5 asserts that there are no others; the following auxiliary statement can be a convenient tool in the proof.

Lemma 16.4. *If a is a diagonal $n \times n$ matrix, and if $w_n(i, j) = \omega^{ij}$, where ω is a primitive n-th root of unity, then*

$$\| |w_n a| \| = \sqrt{n}\, \|a\|_2.$$

▶ The computation is straightforward: if $a = \text{diag}(\alpha_1, \ldots, \alpha_n)$, then the rows of $|w_n a|$ are all equal to $\langle |\alpha_1|, \ldots, |\alpha_n| \rangle$, and consequently

$$\||w_n a|\| = \sup \left\{ \left(n \left| \sum_{j=1}^{n} |\alpha_j| \xi_j \right|^2 \right)^{1/2} : \sum_{j=1}^{n} |\xi_j|^2 \leq 1 \right\}$$

$$= \sqrt{n} \left(\sum_{j=1}^{n} |\alpha_j|^2 \right)^{1/2} = \sqrt{n} \, \|a\|_2. \quad ◀$$

Theorem 16.5. *A matrix is universally absolutely bounded if and only if it is of the form $\lambda + h$, where λ is a scalar and h is a Hilbert-Schmidt matrix.*

▶ (1) If a is universally absolutely bounded, then so is a^* (cf. Corollary 10.6), and, therefore, so also are $a \pm a^*$. If a matrix a is such that both $a \pm a^*$ are of the form $\lambda + h$ (λ a scalar and h a Hilbert-Schmidt matrix), then so is a itself. Consequence: it is both necessary and sufficient to prove the theorem for Hermitian matrices. Since, moreover, the "if" is already known, the rest of the proof assumes that a is a universally absolutely bounded Hermitian matrix and proves that a has the desired form.

(2) If λ is in the essential spectrum of a, then $a - \lambda$ is Hermitian and has 0 in its essential spectrum, and therefore (Lemma 15.6) there exists a Hilbert-Schmidt matrix c such that $(a - \lambda) - c$ is unitarily equivalent to a diagonal matrix that has a large 0 direct summand. Since a, λ, and c are universally absolutely bounded, so is $(a - \lambda) - c$; this reduces the proof to the case $\lambda = 0$, $c = 0$.

(3) Suppose, therefore, that b is a diagonal matrix such that $b \oplus 0$ is universally absolutely bounded (where both the direct summands b and 0 are "large"); it is to be proved that b is a Hilbert-Schmidt matrix. The next step is to use the same device as in step (2) of the proof of Theorem 16.1 to prove that the product of b and any bounded matrix is absolutely bounded. Indeed: if p is a matrix with $\|p\| \leq 1$, then find matrices r, s, t so that $u = \begin{pmatrix} p & r \\ s & t \end{pmatrix}$ is unitary, and infer that pbp^* is absolutely bounded. Since scalar factors do not alter absolute boundedness, pbp^* is absolutely bounded no matter what the norm of p is. Apply this result to $p + 1$ and to $p + i$ and conclude that both $pb \pm bp^*$ are absolutely bounded. Conclusion: if p is an arbitrary bounded matrix, both pb and bp^* are absolutely bounded. (More is true, just as in the proof of Theorem 16.1, but the present proof not even all of this will be needed.)

(4) So far the proof did not exploit the diagonal character of b; the time has come to do so. If $b = \text{diag} \langle \beta_1, \beta_2, \beta_3, \ldots \rangle$, it is to be proved that $\sum_n |\beta_n|^2 < \infty$. The main tool in the proof is Lemma 16.4, which converts absolute boundedness into square summability.

If $\sum_n |\beta_n|^2 = \infty$, then there exist integers $n_0, n_1, n_2, \ldots$ such that

$$0 = n_0 < n_1 < n_2 < \cdots$$

and

$$\sum_{j=n_{k-1}+1}^{n_k} |\beta_j|^2 \geq k^2 \quad \text{for } k = 1, 2, 3, \ldots.$$

110

If $u_n = \dfrac{1}{\sqrt{n}} w_n$ (where the w's are the matrices described in Lemma 16.4), then each u_n is unitary (cf. Example 10.3), and so therefore is the direct sum

$$u = \sum_{k=1}^{\infty} \oplus u_{(n_k - n_{k-1})}.$$

If b_k is the finite diagonal matrix

$$\operatorname{diag}\langle \beta_{n_{k-1}+1}, \ldots, \beta_{n_k}\rangle,$$

so that

$$b = \sum_{k=1}^{\infty} \oplus b_k,$$

then (by the conclusion of step (3)) ub is absolutely bounded. Since, however,

$$ub = \sum_{k=1}^{\infty} \oplus (u_{(n_k - n_{k-1})} b_k)$$

and since, by Lemma 16.4,

$$\| |u_{(n_k - n_{k-1})} b_k| \| = \left(\sum_{j=n_{k-1}+1}^{n_k} |\beta_j|^2 \right)^{1/2} \geq k,$$

the product ub is not absolutely bounded. The contradiction can be caused by the assumption on $\sum_n |\beta_n|^2$ only, which is therefore untenable; the proof is complete. ◀ [49]

§17. Recognition

Which operators *are* integral operators? This is a more primitive question than the one that asks which operators *can* be integral operators (§15) and the one that asks which operators *must* be integral operators (§16). The problem is one of recognition: if an integral operator on $L^2(X)$ is described in some manner other than by its kernel, how do its operatorial and measure-theoretic properties reflect the existence of a kernel that induces it? (Cf. Problem 8.2.) If, for instance, an operator comes presented as the product of two integral operators on $L^2(X)$, when can it be recognized as being itself an integral operator? (Cf. Problem 7.1.) What if the operator is described by its matrix with respect to an orthonormal basis for $L^2(X)$? What if, in particular, the operator acts as a weighted shift on an orthonormal basis for $L^2(X)$? Some operators of all these kinds are integral operators and some are not – how can the ones that are be identified? Emphasis: since the question pertains to the special category of L^2 spaces, not to the more abstract category of Hilbert spaces, the answer must be of the same kind. The answer cannot be expressed in unitarily invariant language, because that would imply that every operator unitarily equivalent to an integral operator is an integral operator also – which is possible over atomic spaces only. The answer, in other words, must be in terms of the relation of the given operator to the underlying measure structure.

The question is one about the class of all bounded kernels on $X \times X$; it asks for the range of the mapping Int, or, a little more vaguely, it asks for a way of determining whether a given operator belongs to that range. This kind of question can be asked about other classes of kernels – e.g., the class of all absolutely bounded kernels, or the class of all bounded Carleman kernels. For the class of all bounded Carleman kernels there is a good answer.

Remark 17.1. ▶ If A is a bounded Carleman operator on $L^2(X)$, then there exists a measurable function Ω on X, $0 \leq \Omega(x) < \infty$ almost everywhere, such that

$$|A g(x)| \leq \|g\| \cdot \Omega(x)$$

almost everywhere for every g in $L^2(X)$. (Cf. Example 12.4.) Indeed: since A is a Carleman operator, there exists a Carleman function $\gamma: X \to L^2(X)$ such that

$$A g(x) = (g, \gamma(x))$$

almost everywhere; set

$$\Omega(x) = \|\gamma(x)\|.$$

In a descriptive phrase: a Carleman operator is pointwise dominated (or, perhaps better, almost everywhere dominated). Caution: the exceptional set of measure zero, where $|A g(x)| \leqq \|g\| \cdot \Omega(x)$ fails to hold, may depend on g.

The remark yields another proof that if X is divisible, then the identity is not a Carleman operator. The reasoning goes as follows. If E is a measurable set of positive measure, then E includes subsets of arbitrarily small positive measure. A large multiple of the characteristic function of a set of small measure is a function of norm 1. Consequence: the unit ball of $L^2(X)$ contains functions that attain arbitrarily large values within any set of positive measure, and that precludes the existence of a finite upper bound for their absolute values.

Similarly, the remark recaptures the result that if X is divisible, then a Carleman operator on $L^2(X)$ is not invertible (cf. Corollary 11.7). Indeed: if $g \in L^2(X)$, then

$$|g(x)| = |(A^{-1}g, \gamma(x))| \leqq \|A^{-1}\| \cdot \|g\| \cdot \|\gamma(x)\|,$$

and the conclusion is inferred as in the preceding paragraph. Still another application of the technique can be used to recapture the result that if X is divisible, then a multiplication operator induced by a non-zero multiplier cannot be a Carleman operator. With a modicum of care with the proofs, the first two results (identity and invertibility) extend from divisible spaces to not atomic ones. The last result (multiplication operators) extends also, but it has to be reformulated slightly: the correct assertion is that if φ is a bounded measurable function such that $\{x: \varphi(x) \neq 0\}$ includes a divisible subset of positive measure, then M_φ is not a Carleman operator. ◀

The condition of pointwise domination is in exactly the right spirit (not unitarily invariant but appropriate to the measure-theoretic structure of the underlying space); it is pleasant to know that it is not only necessary for the Carleman property, but sufficient also.

Theorem 17.2. *An operator A on $L^2(X)$ is a Carleman operator if and only if there exists a measurable function Ω on X, $0 \leqq \Omega(x) < \infty$ almost everywhere, such that*

$$|A g(x)| \leqq \|g\| \cdot \Omega(x)$$

almost everywhere for every g in $L^2(X)$.

▶ "Only if" is settled by Remark 17.1.

Suppose now that the condition of pointwise domination is satisfied; assume, with no loss, that $\Omega(x) > 0$ for every x. Let $\{e_n\}$ be a countable orthonormal basis for $L^2(X)$, let L be the linear manifold of all finite linear combinations of the e's, and let L_0 be the (countable) subset consisting of all finite linear combinations with (complex) rational coefficients.

The major stumbling block in this proof is the possible presence of too many sets of measure zero; it is important to keep track of them, and to make sure that only countably many of them intervene. For this reason it becomes necessary to take a rare point of view, namely, to recall that the elements of $L^2(X)$ are not functions but equivalence classes of functions modulo sets of measure zero.

For each n, let e'_n be a function in the equivalence class $A e_n$, and, for each g in L, $g = \sum_{i=1}^{n} \alpha_i e_i$, write $g' = \sum_{i=1}^{n} \alpha_i e'_i$. The assumption of pointwise domination implies the existence of a set E of measure zero in X such that if $g \in L_0$ (a countable set) and if $x \notin E$, then

$$|g'(x)| \leq \|g\| \cdot \Omega(x).$$

Assertion: if $x \notin E$, then $|g'(x)| \leq \|g\| \cdot \Omega(x)$ for each g in L. To prove that, consider an arbitrary $g = \sum_{i=1}^{n} \alpha_i e_i$ in L, and let ε be an arbitrary positive number. Given a point x_0 not in E, find rational numbers ρ_i so that $|\rho_i| \leq |\alpha_i|$ and $|\alpha_i - \rho_i| \leq \dfrac{\varepsilon}{n \Omega(x_0)}$, $i = 1, \ldots, n$. It follows that if $h = \sum_{i=1}^{n} \rho_i e_i (\in L_0)$, then

$$|g'(x_0)| = \left| \sum_{i=1}^{n} \alpha_i e'_i(x_0) \right|$$

$$\leq \left| \sum_{i=1}^{n} \rho_i e'_i(x_0) \right| + \sum_{i=1}^{n} |\alpha_i - \rho_i| \cdot |e'_i(x_0)|$$

$$\leq |h'(x_0)| + \varepsilon \leq \|h\| \cdot \Omega(x_0) + \varepsilon$$

$$\leq \|g\| \cdot \Omega(x_0) + \varepsilon.$$

(The last step used the relation $|\rho_i| \leq |\alpha_i|$, $i = 1, \ldots, n$.) Since ε is arbitrary, it follows, as asserted, that

$$|g'(x_0)| \leq \|g\| \cdot \Omega(x_0)$$

whenever $x_0 \notin E$.

For each x_0 not in E, the mapping $g \mapsto g'(x_0)$ is a linear functional on L. (Reason: $g \mapsto g'$ is, by definition, the "linearization" of the mapping $e_n \mapsto e'_n$.) By the preceding paragraph, that linear functional is bounded by $\Omega(x_0)$. Since L is dense in $L^2(X)$, the linear functional can be uniquely extended to $L^2(X)$, with the same bound. It follows from the Riesz representation theorem that there exists a unique vector $\gamma(x_0)$ in $L^2(X)$ such that

$$g'(x_0) = (g, \gamma(x_0))$$

for all g in L. Since the function $x \mapsto (g, \gamma(x))$ is measurable for each g in the dense set L, the same is true for each g in $L^2(X)$, and, therefore, the function γ is (weakly) measurable. Since $A g(x) = g'(x)$ almost everywhere when $g \in L$, it follows that $A g(x) = (g, \gamma(x))$ almost everywhere for each g in $L^2(X)$. Conclusion: A is the Carleman operator induced by the Carleman function γ, and the proof is complete. ◄

Corollary 17.3. *An operator A on $L^2(X)$ is a Hilbert-Schmidt operator if and only if there exists a function Ω in $L^2(X)$, $0 \leq \Omega < \infty$, such that, for each g in $L^2(X)$,*

$$|A g(x)| \leq \|g\| \cdot \Omega(x)$$

almost everywhere.

▶ This is an immediate consequence of the fact that the Carleman operator induced by a Carleman function γ is a Hilbert-Schmidt operator if and only if $\|\gamma\| \in L^2(X)$. (Recall that the norm of each linear functional $g \mapsto (g, \gamma(x))$ is $\|\gamma(x)\|$.) ◀[50]

Problem 17.4. *Is there a characterization of integral operators in terms of the existence of a suitable function Ω that in some sense dominates all the functions A g (for g in L^2)?* The question is vague; there doesn't seem to be any natural candidate for the kind of function (and the kind of domination?) that would do. For Hilbert-Schmidt operators, square integrable functions are the answer (Corollary 17.3), and, for Carleman operators, arbitrary measurable functions (Theorem 17.2); what does that leave for bounded but otherwise unrestricted integral operators? The same sort of questions can and should be raised for integral operators induced by absolutely bounded kernels. ◀

There is another pointwise characterization of Carleman operators that asserts that they do almost everywhere what Hilbert-Schmidt operators do in the norm.

Theorem 17.5. *An operator A on $L^2(X)$ is a Carleman operator if and only if, for each orthonormal set $\{e_n\}$ for $L^2(X)$, the series $\sum_n |A e_n(x)|^2$ converges almost everywhere.*

If A is a Carleman operator, and if $\{e_n\}$ and $\{f_n\}$ are orthonormal bases for $L^2(X)$, then $\sum_n |A e_n(x)|^2 = \sum_n |A f_n(x)|^2$ almost everywhere.

▶ If A is the Carleman operator induced by a Carleman function γ,

$$A g(x) = (g, \gamma(x))$$

almost everywhere, and if $\{e_n\}$ is an orthonormal basis for $L^2(X)$, then $A e_n(x)$ is, for almost every x, the complex conjugate of the Fourier coefficient of $\gamma(x)$ with respect to the basis $\{e_n\}$, and, consequently,

$$\sum_n |A e_n(x)|^2 = \|\gamma(x)\|^2$$

almost everywhere. This proves both the "only if" of the first assertion and the entire second assertion.

To prove "if", take an arbitrary orthonormal basis $\{e_n\}$ for $L^2(X)$ and write

$$\Omega(x) = \sqrt{\sum_n |A e_n(x)|^2}.$$

If $g \in L^2(X)$, $g = \sum_n \alpha_n e_n$, then $A g = \sum_n \alpha_n A e_n$, and therefore

$$|A g(x)| \leq \sum_n |\alpha_n| \cdot |A e_n(x)|$$

almost everywhere. (A subsequence of the sequence of partial sums of $\sum_n \alpha_n A e_n(x)$ converges to $A g(x)$ almost everywhere.) Consequence:

$$|A g(x)| \leq (\sum_n |\alpha_n|^2)^{\frac{1}{2}} \cdot (\sum_n |A e_n(x)|^2)^{\frac{1}{2}} = \|g\| \cdot \Omega(x),$$

and Theorem 17.2 implies that A is a Carleman operator. ◀ [51]

Problem 17.6. ▶ One of the principal features that distinguish between the special case of Carleman kernels and bounded kernels in general is the collection of sets of measure zero that have to be avoided. If k is a Carleman kernel, then there exists *one* set E of measure zero in X such that $k(x, \cdot) \in L^2$ whenever $x \notin E$ (and hence such that $k(x, \cdot) g \in L^1$ whenever $x \notin E$ and $g \in L^2$). If, on the other hand, all that is known is that k is a bounded kernel, then for each g in L^2 there is a set $F(g)$ of measure zero in X such that $k(x, \cdot) g \in L^1$ whenever $x \notin F(g)$ (cf. Example 11.1); many of the troubles of the subject are caused by the possibility that the union of the $F(g)$'s may be too large. The most restrictive condition of all is, of course, satisfied by the Hilbert-Schmidt kernels; for them the L^2 norm $\|k(x, \cdot)\|$, as a function of x, is square integrable.

If A is a Hilbert-Schmidt operator on $L^2(X)$ and $\{e_n\}$ is an orthonormal basis, then the ℓ^2 norm of the sequence $\{A e_n(x)\}$ is finite almost everywhere, and, in fact, as a function of x, it is square integrable; this property characterizes Hilbert-Schmidt operators. By Theorem 17.5, if A is a Carleman operator and $\{e_n\}$ is an orthonormal basis, then there exists one set E of measure zero such that $\sum_n |A e_n(x)|^2 < \infty$ whenever $x \notin E$ (and hence $\sum_n |\alpha_n A e_n(x)| < \infty$ whenever $x \notin E$ and $\alpha \in \ell^2$); this property characterizes Carleman operators. Based on these half sequential and half functional analogues to known facts, the following question looks reasonable: *are integral operators A characterized by the condition that if $\{e_n\}$ is an orthonormal basis and α is a sequence in ℓ^2, then there exists a set $F(\alpha)$ of measure zero such that $\sum_n |\alpha_n A e_n(x)| < \infty$ whenever $x \notin F(\alpha)$?*

An affirmative answer to the question would have a pleasant consequence: it would imply that the set of all integral operators on $L^2(X)$ is always a right ideal, and thus solve Problem 11.8. The reasoning is simple. If A is such that $\sum_n |\alpha_n A e_n(x)| < \infty$ almost everywhere whenever $\alpha \in \ell^2$ and $\{e_n\}$ is an orthonormal basis, and if U is a unitary operator, then it follows that $\sum_n |\alpha_n A U e_n(x)| < \infty$ almost everywhere also. (Reason: $\{U e_n\}$ is an orthonormal basis.) This says that the operator AU satisfies the presumed characteristic condition for being integral, so that AU is integral whenever A is. Since every operator B is a linear combination of four unitary operators, it follows that AB is integral whenever A is.

116

Once that is known, the argument in the proof of Theorem 11.11 could be repeated, with obvious minor modifications, to prove that the adjoint of every normal integral operator is integral (Problem 11.12).

Final comment: since $\sum_n |A e_n(x)|^2 < \infty$ is known to be a characteristic property of Carleman operators, the reasoning of the preceding paragraph gives an alternative proof of the right-ideal theorem for those operators (11.6). ◀

For Carleman operators the recognition problem is solved by Theorem 17.2 and, in a different way, by Theorem 17.5. These solutions are of interest not only for what they say, but for the directions they point in; they offer hope for a solution of the recognition problem for arbitrary integral operators (cf. Problems 17.4 and 17.6). The following third solution is recorded here for the same two reasons.

Theorem 17.7. *An operator A on $L^2(X)$ is a Carleman operator if and only if it maps every norm null-sequence onto an almost everywhere null-sequence (i.e., $\|g_n\| \to 0$ implies $A g_n(x) \to 0$ almost everywhere).*

▶ "Only if" is trivial: if $A g(x) = (g, \gamma(x))$, then

$$|A g_n(x)| \leq \|g_n\| \cdot \|\gamma(x)\|.$$

The proof of "if" is straightforward, but quite a few indices seem to be needed to get it right. In view of Theorem 17.5, it is to be proved that if $\|g_n\| \to 0$ implies $A g_n(x) \to 0$ almost everywhere, and if $\{e_n\}$ is an orthonormal set, then $\sum_n |A e_n(x)|^2 < \infty$ almost everywhere. Suppose, therefore, that the conclusion is false. It follows that there exists a measurable set M of positive finite measure such that $\sum_n |A e_n(x)|^2 = \infty$ almost everywhere in M. Discard the exceptional set of measure zero; if x is in the M that remains, and if $p = 1, 2, 3, \ldots$, then

$$(*) \qquad \sum_{n=1}^{q} |A e_n(x)|^2 \geq p^2$$

for some $q = q(p, x)$. If $M_p(q)$ is the set of x's in M for which $(*)$ holds, then

$$M_p(1) \subset M_p(2) \subset M_p(3) \subset \cdots \to M$$

for each p. If q_p is chosen so that $M_p(q_p)$ is very near to M $\left(\mu(M_p(q_p)) > \left(1 - \frac{1}{3^p}\right)\mu(M)\right.$ will do$\left.\right)$, then the set

$$M_0 = \bigcap_p M_p(q_p)$$

has positive measure. The set M_0 has all the good properties of M, and it has, moreover, the additional good property that if $x \in M_0$ and $p = 1, 2, 3, \ldots$, then

$$\sum_{n=1}^{q_p} |A e_n(x)|^2 \geq p^2.$$

For each p, a function F_p from M_0 to $\mathbb{C}^{q_p}$ is defined by

$$F_p(x) = \langle A\,e_1(x), \ldots, A\,e_{q_p}(x) \rangle;$$

the important property of F_p is that

$$\|F_p(x)\| \geq p$$

for all p and for all x in M_0. $\left(\text{The norm } \|F_p(x)\| \text{ is the Euclidean norm}\right.$
$\left.\left(\sum_{n=1}^{q_p} |A\,e_n(x)|^2\right)^{\frac{1}{2}} \text{ in } \mathbb{C}^{q_p}.\right)$

Observe now that in any finite-dimensional Hilbert space the sets

$$U_f = \{g : |(f,g)| > 1\},$$

with $\|f\| \leq 2/p$, constitute an open cover of the sphere $\{g : \|g\| = p\}$. (Given g with $\|g\| = p$, put $f = 2g/p^2$; then $\|f\| = 2/p$ and $|(f,g)| = 2$.) Compactness yields the existence of a finite subcover. Conclusion: for each p, there exists a finite set $\{f_p(1), \ldots, f_p(k_p)\}$ of vectors in $\mathbb{C}^{q_p}$ such that $\|f_p(j)\| \leq 2/p, j = 1, \ldots, k_p$, and such that, for each x in M_0, $|(f_p(j), F_p(x))| > 1$ for at least one j. (If $\|F_p(x)\| = p$, then there is a j such that $|(f_p(j), F_p(x))| > 1$; if $\|F_p(x)\| > p$, apply this statement to $pF_p(x)/\|F_p(x)\|$ in place of $F_p(x)$.) Since $\mathbb{C}^{q_p}$ comes equipped with a coordinate system, it is convenient to rephrase the conclusion in terms of coordinates: for each p, there exist vectors

$$\langle f_p^1(j), \ldots, f_p^{q_p}(j) \rangle, \quad j = 1, \ldots, k_p,$$

in $\mathbb{C}^{q_p}$ such that

$$\left(\sum_{n=1}^{q_p} |f_p^n(j)|^2\right)^{\frac{1}{2}} \leq \frac{2}{p},$$

and such that, for each x in M_0,

$$\left|\sum_{n=1}^{q_p} f_p^n(j)\,A\,e_n(x)\right| > 1$$

for at least one j. (The missing complex conjugation on $A\,e_n(x)$ can be absorbed in the $f_p^n(j)$'s.)

Write $g_p(j) = \sum_{n=1}^{q_p} f_p^n(j)\,e_n$. It follows that

$$\|g_p(j)\| \leq \frac{2}{p},$$

and that, for each x in M_0, there exists a $j\,(=1, \ldots, k_p)$ with

$$|A\,g_p(j)(x)| > 1.$$

String the finite sequences $\langle g_p(j) : j = 1, \ldots, k_p \rangle$ one after another to get a norm null-sequence

$$\langle g_1, g_2, g_3, \ldots \rangle$$
$$= \langle g_1(1), \ldots, g_1(k_1), g_2(1), \ldots, g_2(k_2), g_3(1), \ldots \rangle \quad \text{in } L^2(X).$$

If $x \in M_0$, then there are arbitrarily large values of n such that $|A g_n(x)| > 1$, i.e., $A g_n(x)$ does not converge to 0 at any point of M_0. A contradiction has arrived; the proof is complete. ◄ 52

Appendix A
Finiteness and Countability Conditions

The condition of σ-finiteness (F) has a useful weaker form (L): a measure space is *locally finite* if every set of positive measure includes a set of positive finite measure. Similarly, there is a countability condition (C) that is in most of its applications weaker than separability (S): a measure space is *countably decomposable* (or satisfies the *countable chain condition*) if every disjoint collection of sets of positive measure is countable. The study of these conditions and of the implications among them has very little to do with integral operators, but a brief digression in that direction may be of interest.

The facts are summarized by the diagram:

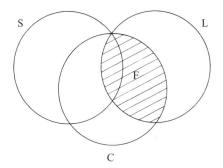

Explicitly:

(1) $\qquad L\,\&\,C \Leftrightarrow F,$

(2) $\qquad S\,\&\,L \Rightarrow C,$

and nothing else can be said.

In the direction $F \Rightarrow L$ and $F \Rightarrow C$ the proof of (1) is trivial. To prove $L\,\&\,C \Rightarrow F$, consider a maximal disjoint collection of sets of positive finite measure; by C, it's countable; by L, its union must be almost all the space. For (2): if a disjoint collection of sets of positive measure is uncountable, then, for some ε, uncountably many of them have subsets with finite measures $\geq \varepsilon > 0$; the characteristic functions of those subsets contradict separability.

To prove that there are no other implications, it is necessary to construct seven examples. That can be done in terms of the following five primitive measure spaces.

120

Let X_0 be a finite atom, i.e., a measure space consisting of a single point of measure 1, say. Let X_1 be an infinite atom, i.e., a measure space consisting of a single point of measure ∞. (Note that X_1 is separable, because $L^2(X_1)$ is 0-dimensional.) Let X_∞ be an uncountable set, let every subset of X_∞ be measurable, and let the measure be defined as 0 for the countable sets and ∞ for the uncountable ones. (This space too has a 0-dimensional L^2.) Let Y_0 be the Cartesian product of uncountably many 2-point spaces (in each of which both points carry positive mass and the total measure is 1). Let Y_1 be an uncountable set, let every subset of Y_1 be measurable, and let the measure of a set be defined as the number of points in it (the *counting measure*).

The desired examples are now easy to describe. (The dashes indicate negation, and juxtaposition indicates conjunction, so that, for instance, $S'L'C'$ is the description of a space that is not separable, not locally finite, and not countably decomposable.)

$S'L'C'$: the disjoint union $X_1 \cup Y_1$.

$S'L'C$: the disjoint union $X_1 \cup Y_0$.

$S'LC'$: Y_1.

$S'LC$: Y_0.

SC': X_∞.

$SL'C$: X_1.

SLC: X_0.

Observe, in particular, that Y_0 exemplifies $S'F$, and X_∞ exemplifies not only SF' and SL' but even SC'.

Appendix B
Pointwise Unbounded Bounded Kernels

A powerful tool of analysis is to get information about unbounded functions by the study of their bounded truncations: given f, define $f_n(x) = f(x)$ or 0 according as $|f(x)| \leq n$ or not, and note that $f_n(x) \to f(x)$ for every x. The version of this approach that would be most useful in the study of integral operators is false beyond redemption: some kernels not only fail to be pointwise bounded themselves but do not even have any non-trivial pointwise bounded subkernels. The latter is an ad hoc word, but perhaps it suggests its meaning: a *subkernel* of k (on $X \times Y$) is the restriction of k to a measurable rectangle $X_0 \times Y_0$.

Theorem B1. *There exists a measurable function on $\mathbb{R} \times \mathbb{R}$ that is essentially unbounded on every measurable rectangle of positive measure.*

"Essentially" refers, as usual, to a property that is unaffected by alterations on a set of measure zero.

▶ Let $r_1, r_2, \ldots$ be an enumeration of the rational numbers, and let I_n be the open interval with center r_n and radius $1/2^n$, $n = 1, 2, 3, \ldots$. The set of real numbers that belong to I_n for infinitely many values of n form a set of measure zero. It follows that if χ_n is the characteristic function of I_n, then the sequence $\{\chi_1(x), \chi_2(x), \ldots\}$ is finitely non-zero for almost every x. This implies that the series

$$\varphi(x) = \sum_{n=1}^{\infty} \frac{\chi_n(x)}{|x - r_n|}$$

converges at almost every x. The sum defines an almost-everywhere finite-valued Borel measurable function that is essentially unbounded on every non-empty open set. [Note: the construction could have been carried out with $1/x^2$ or $1/\sqrt{x}$ in place of $1/x$, and, in fact, with every function that is essentially unbounded near 0.] Write

$$k(x, y) = \varphi(x - y);$$

the theorem will be proved by showing that k is an almost-everywhere finite-valued measurable function that is essentially unbounded on every measurable rectangle of positive measure.

If δ is the mapping from $\mathbb{R} \times \mathbb{R}$ to $\mathbb{R}$ defined by

$$\delta(x, y) = x - y,$$

then $k = \varphi \circ \delta$, which proves that k is measurable. If $E = \{x \in \mathbb{R} : \varphi(x) = \infty\}$ $(= \varphi^{-1}(\infty))$, then $k^{-1}(\infty) = \delta^{-1}(E)$. Since E is a Borel set in $\mathbb{R}$, the inverse image $\delta^{-1}(E)$ is a Borel set in $\mathbb{R} \times \mathbb{R}$. Since E has measure 0 (because φ is finite almost everywhere), and since

$$\{x : \langle x, y \rangle \in \delta^{-1}(E)\} = \{x : x - y \in E\} = E + y$$

for each y in $\mathbb{R}$, it follows that each horizontal section of $\delta^{-1}(E)$ has measure 0, and hence, by Fubini's theorem, that $\delta^{-1}(E)$ has measure 0. Consequence: k is finite almost everywhere.

Fix a (large) positive number M, and, for each $n = 1, 2, 3, \ldots$, consider the points $\langle x, y \rangle$ for which

$$\frac{\chi_n(x - y)}{|x - y - r_n|} > M.$$

These are the points $\langle x, y \rangle$ for which $x - y \in I_n \cap J_n$, where J_n is the open interval with center r_n and radius $1/M$.

If D is the (dense) open set $\bigcup_n (I_n \cap J_n)$, then

$$k^{-1}((M, \infty)) \supset \bigcup_n \left\{(x, y) : \frac{\chi_n(x - y)}{|x - y - r_n|} > M\right\} = \delta^{-1}(D).$$

To prove the theorem, it is therefore sufficient to prove that, for each M, the set $\delta^{-1}(D)$ meets every measurable rectangle of positive measure in a set of positive measure.

Suppose that $E \times F$ is a measurable rectangle of positive measure. Assertion: $D \cap (E - F)$ includes a non-empty open set (and, therefore, has positive measure). To prove the assertion, note that there exists a set G of positive measure, and there exist real numbers α and β, such that $G + \alpha \subset E$ and $G + \beta \subset F$. It follows that $E - F \supset (G - G) + (\alpha - \beta)$, and hence that $E - F$ includes a non-empty open set. This, in turn, implies that $D \cap (E - F)$ includes a set of the same kind.

The proof of the theorem will be completed by showing that

$$\lambda(\delta^{-1}(D) \cap (E \times F)) > 0,$$

where $\lambda = \mu \otimes \mu$ is planar Lebesgue measure. Assume (with no loss of generality) that every point of E is a point of density for E, and the same for F. Let I be a non-empty open interval included in $D \cap (E - F)$, and choose $\langle x_0, y_0 \rangle$ in $E \times F$ so that $x_0 - y_0 \in I$. Since x_0 is a point of density for E and since $x_0 \in I + y_0$, it follows that $\mu((D + y_0) \cap E) \geq \mu((I + y_0) \cap E) > 0$.

Since the function $y \mapsto \mu((I + y) \cap E)$ is continuous, there exists an open interval J containing y_0 such that $\mu((D + y) \cap E) > 0$ for every y in J. Since y_0 is a point of density for F, and since $y_0 \in J$, it follows that $\mu(J \cap F) > 0$. Conclusion: the set of those points y in F for which $\mu((D + y) \cap E) > 0$ has positive measure. For each real number y

$$(\delta^{-1}(D)\cap(E\times F))^y=\{x:\langle x,y\rangle\in\delta^{-1}(D)\cap(E\times F)\}$$
$$=\{x:\langle x,y\rangle\in\delta^{-1}(D)\}\cap\{x:\langle x,y\rangle\in E\times F\}$$
$$=\begin{cases}(D+y)\cap E & \text{for } y \text{ in } F,\\ \varnothing & \text{for } y \text{ not in } F.\end{cases}$$

Since, therefore,

$$\lambda(\delta^{-1}(D)\cap(E\times F))=\int\mu((\delta^{-1}(D)\cap(E\times F))^y)\,dy$$
$$=\int_F\mu((D+y)\cap E)\,dy,$$

the desired inequality follows from the conclusion of the preceding paragraph. ◀ [53]

Corollary B2. *There exists a planar set of positive measure that includes no measurable rectangle of positive measure.*

▶ For M sufficiently large, the set $\{\langle x,y\rangle: k(x,y)<M\}$ has positive measure. ◀ [54]

Corollary B3. *There exists a square integrable kernel that is essentially unbounded on every measurable rectangle of positive measure.*

▶ The idea is to use a kernel k of the kind whose existence Theorem B1 asserts, and to modify it so as to make it square integrable. It is convenient to restrict k to $\mathbb{II}\times\mathbb{II}$ (instead of $\mathbb{R}\times\mathbb{R}$); the restriction clearly inherits all the relevant (measurability and unboundedness) properties of the original k.

Write $M_0=0$ and choose M_n $(n=1,2,3,\ldots)$ inductively so that

$$M_n>\max\{n, M_{n-1}\},$$
$$\lambda(\{\langle x,y\rangle: M_{n-1}<|k(x,y)|\leq M_n\})>0,$$
$$\lambda(\{\langle x,y\rangle: |k(x,y)|\leq M_n\})>1-\frac{1}{2^n}.$$

If $C_n=\{\langle x,y\rangle: M_n<|k(x,y)|\leq M_{n+1}\}$, then $0<\lambda(C_n)<\dfrac{1}{2^n}$ for $n=1,2,3,\ldots$. Define h by

$$h(x,y)=\sum_n 2^{n/4}\chi_{C_n}(x,y).$$

Since the C_n's are pairwise disjoint, so that their characteristic functions are pairwise orthogonal, it follows that

$$\|h\|_2^2=\sum_n\|2^{n/4}\chi_{C_n}\|_2^2=\sum_n 2^{n/2}\lambda(C_n)\leq\sum_n 2^{n/2}\frac{1}{2^n}<\infty,$$

so that h is square integrable.

Assertion: if $E \times F$ is a measurable rectangle of positive measure and $M > 0$, then

$$\lambda((E \times F) \cap \{\langle x, y \rangle : |h(x, y)| > M\}) > 0.$$

The reasoning goes as follows. For each $n (= 1, 2, 3, \ldots)$,

$$0 < \lambda((E \times F) \cap \{\langle x, y \rangle : M_n < |k(x, y)|\})$$
$$= \sum_{m=n}^{\infty} \lambda((E \times F) \cap C_m),$$

and therefore $\lambda((E \times F) \cap C_m) > 0$ for some $m \geq n$. If, in particular, n is so large that $M < 2^{n/4}$, then, of course, $M < 2^{m/4}$, and

$$(E \times F) \cap \{\langle x, y \rangle : |h(x, y)| > M\}$$
$$\supset (E \times F) \cap \{\langle x, y \rangle : |h(x, y)| > 2^{m/4}\})$$
$$\supset (E \times F) \cap C_m;$$

the assertion is proved. ◄

Corollary B3 strengthens Theorem B1: the "bad" kernel can be "small". There is another possible strengthening: try to make the kernel very bad.

Problem B4. ► *Is there a kernel with no non-trivial bounded subkernels?* ("Non-trivial" is intended to exclude restrictions to measurable rectangles of measure 0 only.) Worse yet: *is there a kernel all of whose non-trivial subkernels have domain 0?* ◄ [55]

Appendix C
Riemann-Lebesgue Lemma

Lemma C. *If X is a measure space, if $\{e_n\}$ is a uniformly bounded orthonormal sequence in $L^2(X)$, and if $f \in L^1(X)$, then*

$$\int f(x) e_n(x)\, dx \to 0 \qquad as\ n \to \infty.$$

▶ If $f \in L^2$, the conclusion is trivial: the Fourier coefficients of f (with respect to the complex conjugates $\bar{e}_n$) form a square summable sequence. The assertion for L^1 can be made to depend on the fact that every function in L^1 can be approximated arbitrarily closely, in the L^1 metric, by functions in $L^1 \cap L^2$. (In other words: $L^1 \cap L^2$ is dense in L^1. Reason: the bounded functions supported by sets of finite measure are always dense in L^1. Note that if μ is finite, then $L^2 \subset L^1$; in that case the assertion is that L^2 is dense in L^1.)

The proof of the Riemann-Lebesgue lemma can now be made to go as follows. Normalize (with no loss of generality) so that $|e_n| \leq 1$ almost everywhere for every n. Given $\varepsilon(>0)$, find g in $L^1 \cap L^2$ so that $\|f - g\|_1 < \varepsilon/2$. Since $g \in L^2$, it follows that

$$\left| \int g(x) e_n(x)\, dx \right| < \frac{\varepsilon}{2}$$

as soon as n is sufficiently large. Since

$$\left| \int (f(x) - g(x)) e_n(x)\, dx \right| \leq \|f - g\|_1 < \frac{\varepsilon}{2}$$

for all n, it follows that

$$\left| \int f(x) e_n(x)\, dx \right| < \varepsilon$$

for large n, and the proof is complete. ◀

Notes

1 (p. 3). The basic measure-theoretic concepts and facts can be found in [21]; the representation theorem is on p. 173.

2 (p. 7). The process of inflating a matrix into a kernel on a divisible space was considered by Carleman [8, p. 185].

3 (p. 11). For a discussion of points of density see, for instance, [24, p. 274].

4 (p. 12). The example is more or less the standard example of a non-closeable operator; see [14, p. 55].

5 (p. 13). Carleman [8] restricted most of his attention to Hermitian operators, but much of the theory extends to the general case.

6 (p. 14). Theorem 3.10 is due to Banach [2, p. 87]. Cf. also [26, p. 165] and [10, p. 348].

7 (p. 18). A detailed discussion of Hilbert-Schmidt operators can be found in [40].

8 (p. 22). The first formulation of the Schur test [42] was for matrices only and used the constant functions ($p=q=1$) only. Subsequent references are [1], [2], and [6].

9 (p. 24). For a detailed discussion of the elementary theory of Toeplitz operators see [22, Chapter 20].

10 (p. 29). J. von Neumann mentioned, without proof, the special cases of Corollary 6.3 in which X and X' are finite or infinite intervals [47]. The details for those special cases were later computed by Misra-Speiser-Targonski [34]; the atomic special case received attention in the work of Weidmann [49].

11 (p. 33). It is convenient to have names for the Fourier transforms. The names here used are motivated by the generalizations of those transforms to topological groups. The range of the discrete Fourier transform is L^2 of the discrete group $\mathbb{Z}$; the range of the compact Fourier transform is L^2 of the compact space $\mathbb{II}$. (If addition is interpreted modulo 1, that space is the compact dual group of $\mathbb{Z}$. Equivalently, the range of the compact Fourier transform can be viewed as L^2 of the circle group, the set of complex numbers of absolute value 1.) One word of warning might be needed, however, to avoid terminological confusion: the compact Fourier transform is not a compact operator. It is, in fact, a unitary map from $L^2(\mathbb{Z})$ onto $L^2(\mathbb{II})$ (cf. Example 5.8 and Theorem 7.5).

12 (p. 37). An important special case of Theorem 7.5 (absolutely bounded kernels) is proved by Zaanen [53, p. 229]. For Carleman kernels the result is in [49].

13 (p. 39). An only slightly more special version of Theorem 8.1 is in [53, p. 227].

14 (p. 40). A pathological set such as is needed in Example 8.3 is described in [21, p. 149].

15 (p. 41). Theorem 8.5, in one form or another, has been known for a long time. Its first version seems to be due to von Neumann [46, p. 13]. The proof here used is due to L.J. Wallen (personal communication).

Another proof of Theorem 8.5 is offered in [22, p. 288], but that proof is incomplete. The gap is not easy to find. It is in the tacit assumption that the indefinite integral of the kernel makes sense, i.e., that the kernel, as a function of two variables, is integrable. The error was noted by G.N. Hile, who also gave a delicate measure-theoretic substitute for the argument.

16 (p. 42). A statement and proof of the Riemann-Lebesgue lemma needed in the proof of Theorem 8.6 can be found in Appendix C.

17 (p. 42). Fatou's lemma is in [21, p. 113]. The techniques in the proof of Theorem 8.6 were suggested (personal communication) by J.P. Williams (Riemann-Lebesgue) and D.A. Stegenga (Fatou).

18 (p. 43). The basic facts about tensor products of Hilbert spaces and operators on them

are well enough known, but there does not seem to be any place in the literature where the details are systematically expounded. Helpful references are: [5, § 42], [7], [9, pp. 22–26], [35, Chapter II], [38, p. 197], and [39, p. 298].

19 (p. 46). If T is a Hilbert-Schmidt operator on a Hilbert space H, and if A is an arbitrary bounded operator on H, then both AT and TA are Hilbert-Schmidt operators. This implies that the set of Hilbert-Schmidt operators is a two-sided ideal in the algebra of all bounded operators on H. The first major step in the proof of Theorem 9.3 is a proof of a very slight generalization of this assertion. Pertinent reference: [40, Chapter II].

20 (p. 49). In connection with Corollary 9.10 and Example 9.11 the following question can be asked: which kernels k on $X \times Y$ are "Schur multipliers" in the sense that the Schur product of h and k is bounded for every bounded kernel h on $X \times Y$. Schur [42] proved that if $\{f_i\}$ and $\{g_j\}$ are bounded sequences of vectors, then the matrix b defined by $b(i,j) = (f_i, g_j)$ is a Schur multiplier for matrices. G. Bennett [3] proved that the matrices b obtained that way are the only Schur multipliers for matrices.

21 (p. 52). Littlewood [32] seems to be the first to have used the Hilbert-Toeplitz matrix for essentially the same purpose as in Example 10.1.

22 (p. 53). Pertinent references: [31], [45].

23 (p. 56). The proof of Theorem 10.7 is substantially the same as the one in [53, p. 228].

24 (p. 57). While, to be sure, Theorem 10.8 supersedes Corollary 9.10, the proof of that corollary seemed so appropriate to a discussion of tensor products that the temptation to include it there was irresistible. As for a reference: the facts (for matrices) were discovered by Schur himself [42].

25 (p. 61). The existence of a bounded kernel that is not semi-square-integrable (Example 11.1) is surprising, and even von Neumann overlooked it [47, p. 17].

26 (p. 63). For a discussion of the measurability of functions with values in a Banach space, and, in particular, a proof that if the range space is separable, then weak and strong measurability are the same, see [25, p. 73].

27 (p. 64). Is Theorem 11.4 in the literature? The source for the proof in the text is M. Schreiber and A.L. Shields (personal communication, 1963).

28 (p. 64). Carleman kernels in general (including unbounded ones) and Theorem 11.5 in particular are discussed in detail in [48]. The elegant device that reduces the proof of Theorem 11.5 to the Hilbert-Schmidt case was taken from that source. Another pertinent reference is [10, p. 198].

29 (p. 66). The original reference for Theorem 11.6 is [44].

30 (p. 69). For the facts about the polar decomposition needed in the proof of Theorem 11.10 see [22, Problems 105 and 108]; for the Fuglede theorem see [16, p. 68].

31 (p. 72). The result about the bounded action of L^1 on L^p via convolutions is a standard part of harmonic analysis; see, for instance, [23, § 20].

32 (p. 74). The Haar functions were introduced by Haar [15].

33 (p. 75). In a different context an example of a non-integral compact operator was given by Fremlin [13].

34 (p. 83). A discussion of Hille-Tamarkin operators can be found in [26, p. 168].

35 (p. 83). For Schauder's theorem see [10, p. 485]. For $\langle p, q \rangle$ compactness: [33] (mainly about absolutely bounded kernels), and [30] (an exhaustive treatise).

36 (p. 84). Theorem 13.8 occurs in the work of Korotkov [28] (relying, in part, on an absolute continuity theorem of Nikishin [36]), and, explicitly and in full detail, in [43].

37 (p. 86). There is a brief treatment of the spectra of direct sums in [22; Problem 81]. For the spectra of tensor products see [7].

38 (p. 86). The first to call attention to the relation between the spectrum of a matrix and the spectrum of its inflation was von Neumann; see [47, p. 6].

39 (p. 87). The usual formulation of Atkinson's theorem (cf. [22, Problem 142]) is for two-sided invertibility, but all it takes to get the sharper and more useful one-sided version is some care with the usual proof.

40 (p. 89). Fillmore, Stampfli, and Williams [12] gave a useful discussion of several equivalent formulations of essential invertibility.

41 (p. 90). There is an efficient discussion of spectra in Banach algebras in [5, § 5].

42 (p. 91). Reference: Weyl [50], and von Neumann [47, Theorem 1, p. 11].

43 (p. 94). The extension of the Weyl theorem to normal operators was discovered by Berg [4]; cf. [19] and [20]. For quasidiagonal and quasitriangular operators see [17] and [18].

44 (p. 99). Theorem 15.1 for Hermitian Carleman operators and Theorem 15.7 for Hermitian operators are von Neumann's main contribution to this subject [47]. Their extension to Carleman operators that are not necessarily Hermitian was noted by Weidmann [49]. The extension of Theorem 15.1 to integral operators in general was made in [43].

45 (p. 101). Weidmann [49, p. 26] gives an example of a product UA that is not a Carleman operator, with U unitary and A a Carleman operator; in that example, however, the operator A is not bounded.

46 (p. 103). Theorems 15.11 and 15.14 were inspired by closely related results of Korotkov [29]; those results apply to Carleman operators only.

47 (p. 108). The Carleman version of Theorem 16.1 was first noted by Targonski [44]; see Weidmann [48]. The present strengthening can be found in [28]. The dilation theorem used in the proof is an easy exercise; see [22, Problem 177].

48 (p. 108). The first question in Problem 16.3 was raised by L.J. Wallen. Questions like that can be raised for special classes of kernels (e.g., Carleman kernels and absolutely bounded ones), but almost nothing seems to be known about the answers. The absolutely bounded question for matrices (i.e., kernels over atomic spaces) is the only one that has been settled. It turns out that if a is a bounded matrix that is not universally absolutely bounded, then the unitary matrices that transform a to an absolutely bounded matrix constitute a set of the first category in the set of all unitary matrices. In particular, the interior of that set must be empty.

49 (p. 110). Reference: [43].

50 (p. 114). Theorem 17.2 is due to Korotkov [27]. Some pertinent observations about not necessarily bounded Carleman operators were made by Wong, [51] and [52].

51 (p. 115). Reference: Schreiber-Targonski [41].

52 (p. 118). Reference: Weidmann [49, p. 14].

53 (p. 123). The proof of Theorem B1 depends on several measure-theoretic details; they can all be found in [21]. Specifically: for the finiteness of φ, see p. 40, Exercise 6, and the Borel-Cantelli lemma, p. 201, Exercise 4; for the positiveness of $\mu(D \cap (E - F))$, see p. 260, Theorem E and p. 68, Theorem B; for the continuity of $\mu((D + y) \cap E)$, see p. 266, Theorem A and p. 268, Exercise 1.

54 (p. 123). The main idea for Theorem B1 is in the original proof of Corollary B2, which is due to Erdös and Oxtoby [11]; cf. also Oxtoby [37].

55 (p. 124). For kernels satisfying some mild boundedness conditions, partial information about Problem B4 can be inferred from the work of Nikishin [36].

References

1. Aronszajn, N., Mulla, F., Szeptycki, P.: On spaces of potentials connected with L^p-spaces. Ann. Inst. Fourier (Grenoble) **12**, 211–306 (1963).
2. Banach, S.: Théorie des opérations linéaires. Warszawa 1932.
3. Bennett, G.: Schur multipliers. Duke Math. J. **44**, 603–639 (1977).
4. Berg, I.D.: An extension of the Weyl-von Neumann theorem to normal operators. Trans. Amer. Math. Soc. **160**, 365–371 (1971).
5. Bonsall, F.J., Duncan, J.: Complete normed algebras. Berlin-Heidelberg-New York: Springer 1973.
6. Brown, A., Halmos, P.R., Shields, A.L.: Cesàro operators. Acta Szeged **26**, 125–137 (1965).
7. Brown, A., Pearcy, C.: Spectra of tensor products of operators. Proc. Amer. Math. Soc. **17**, 162–166 (1966).
8. Carleman, T.: Sur les équations intégrales singulières a noyau rèel et symétrique. Uppsala: Almqvist and Wiksells 1923.
9. Dixmier, J.: Les algèbres d' opérateurs dans l'espace Hilbertien. Paris: Gauthier-Villars 1957.
10. Dunford, N., Schwarz, J.T.: Linear operators. Part I. New York: Interscience 1958.
11. Erdös, P., Oxtoby, J.C.: Partitions of the plane into sets having positive measure in every non-null measurable product set. Trans. Amer. Math. Soc. **79**, 91–102 (1955).
12. Fillmore, P.A., Stampfli, J.G., Williams, J.P.: On the essential numerical range, the essential spectrum, and a problem of Halmos. Acta Szeged **33**, 179–192 (1972).
13. Fremlin, D.H.: A positive compact operator. Manuscripta Math. **15**, 323–327 (1975).
14. Goldberg, S.: Unbounded linear operators. New York: McGraw-Hill 1966.
15. Haar, A.: Zur Theorie der orthogonalen Funktionensysteme. Math. Ann. **69**, 331–371 (1910).
16. Halmos, P.R.: Introduction to Hilbert space and the theory of spectral multiplicity. Chelsea, New York 1951.
17. Halmos, P.R.: Quasitriangular operators. Acta Szeged **29**, 283–293 (1968).
18. Halmos, P.R.: Ten problems in Hilbert space. Bull. Amer. Math. Soc. **76**, 887–933 (1970).
19. Halmos, P.R.: Continuous functions of Hermitian operators. Proc. Amer. Math. Soc. **31**, 130–132 (1972).
20. Halmos, P.R.: Limits of shifts. Acta Szeged **34**, 131–139 (1973).
21. Halmos, P.R.: Measure theory. Berlin-Heidelberg-New York: Springer 1974.
22. Halmos, P.R.: A Hilbert space problem book. Berlin-Heidelberg-New York: Springer 1974.
23. Hewitt, E., Ross, K.A.: Abstract harmonic analysis, Vol. I. Berlin-Göttingen-Heidelberg: Springer 1963.
24. Hewitt, E., Stromberg, K.: Real and abstract analysis. Berlin-Heidelberg-New York: Springer 1965.
25. Hille, E., Phillips, R.S.: Functional analysis and semigroups. Providence: Amer. Math. Soc. 1957.
26. Jörgens, K.: Lineare Integraloperatoren. Stuttgart: Teubner 1970.
27. Korotkov, V.B.: Integral operators with Carleman kernels. Dokl. Akad. Nauk SSSR **165**, 1496–1499 (1965).
28. Korotkov, V.B.: Strong integral operators. Math. Notes **16**, 1137–1140 (1974) [Mat. Zametki **16**, 907–912 (1974)].
29. Korotkov, V.B.: The unitary equivalence of linear operators to integral operators. Math. Notes **19**, 364–368 (1976) [Mat. Zametki, **19**, 601–610 (1976)].

30. Krasnoselskii, M.A., Zabreiko, P.P., Pustylnik, E.I., Sbolevskii, P.E.: Integral operators in spaces of summable functions. Leyden: Noordhoff 1976.
31. Kwapien, S., Pelczynski, A.: The main triangle projection in matrix spaces and its applications. Studia Math. **34**, 43 – 68 (1970).
32. Littlewood, J.E.: On bounded bilinear forms in an infinite number of variables. Quart. J. Math. **1**, 167 – 174 (1930).
33. Luxemburg, W.A.J., Zaanen, A.C.: Compactness of integral operators in Banach function spaces. Math. Annalen **149**, 150 – 180 (1963).
34. Misra, B., Speiser, D., Targonski, G.: Integral operators in the theory of scattering. Helv. Phys. Acta **36**, 963 – 980 (1963).
35. Murray, F.J., von Neumann, J.: On rings of operators. Ann. Math. **37**, 116 – 229 (1936).
36. Nikishin, E.M.: Resonance theorems and superlinear operators. Russian Math. Surveys **25**, 125 – 187 (1970). [Uspehi Mat. Nauk **25**, 129 – 191 (1970)].
37. Oxtoby, J.C.: The category and Borel class of certain subsets of L_p. Bull. Amer. Math. Soc. **43**, 245 – 248 (1937).
38. Palais, R. et al.: Seminar on the Atiyah-Singer index theorem. Princeton 1965.
39. Reed, M., Simon, B.: Functional analysis. New York: Academic Press 1972.
40. Schatten, R.: Norm ideals of completely continuous operators. Berlin-Heidelberg-New York: Springer 1970.
41. Schreiber, M., Targonski, G.: Carleman and semi-Carleman operators. Proc. Amer. Math. Soc. **24**, 293 – 299 (1970).
42. Schur, I.: Bemerkungen zur Theorie der Beschränkten Bilinearformen mit unendlich vielen Veränderlichen. J. reine angew. Math. **140**, 1 – 28 (1911).
43. Sunder, V.S.: Characterization theorems for integral operators. Indiana University Dissertation, 1977.
44. Targonski, G.I.: Seminar on functional operators and equations. Berlin-Heidelberg-New York: Springer 1967.
45. Toeplitz, O.: Über eine bei den Dirichletschen Reihen auftretende Aufgabe aus der Theorie der Potenzreihen von unendlichvielen Veränderlichen. Göttinger Nachrichten 417 – 432 (1913).
46. von Neumann, J.: Mathematische Grundlagen der Quantenmechanik. Berlin: Springer 1932.
47. von Neumann, J.: Charakterisierung des Spektrums eines Integraloperators. Paris: Hermann 1935.
48. Weidmann, J.: Strong Carleman operators are of Hilbert-Schmidt type. Bull. Amer. Math. Soc. **74**, 735 – 737 (1968).
49. Weidmann, J.: Carlemanoperatoren. Manuscripta Math. **2**, 1 – 38 (1970).
50. Weyl, H.: Über beschränkte quadratische Formen deren Differenz vollstetig ist. Rend. Circ. Mat. Palermo **27**, 373 – 392 (1909).
51. Wong, T.K.: On a class of absolutely p-summing operators. Studia Math. **39**, 181 – 189 (1971).
52. Wong, T.K.: N^p-operators and semi-Carleman operators. Acta Szeged **33**, 105 – 112 (1972).
53. Zaanen, A.C.: Linear analysis. New York: Interscience 1953.

Index

Ergebnisse der Mathematik und ihrer Grenzgebiete

A Series of Modern Surveys in Mathematics